AUTISM SUCCESS

Helping Those On the
Autism Spectrum Live Successful Lives

AUTISM SUCCESS

Helping Those On the
Autism Spectrum Live Successful Lives

PAUL MEIER

Dedicated to Mom and Dad.

Table of Contents

INTRODUCTION:
MY LIFE

NOT SUPPOSED TO MAKE IT.

I was not supposed to make it. I am autistic. I also have diagnoses of: anxiety, PTSD, sensory integration disorder, sensory processing disorder, severe dysgraphia, synesthesia, and have symptoms of dyscalculia and mild dyslexia.

I wasn't supposed to make it through high school. Certainly not through college, and presumably would have employment and other life difficulties. Fortunately no one ever told me any of this until I was in my mid-thirties and had already done it. My mom still tells me decades later that she was sure they would be picking me up partway through my freshman year of college. Looking back myself – at the progress notes, report cards, projects, and all the memories of my challenges in life – I agree. I shouldn't have made it, and many times almost didn't. Now I am an autism professional. I routinely help people on the autism spectrum who were never supposed to make it to live successful lives.

I grew up in an unusual home. People tell me my childhood home life was like the television show *Leave it to Beaver*. Honestly, that would have been comparably high stress and conflict. My home was better than that. Not only did my parents never fight with each other, they never even disagreed with each other in front of us kids. I was never yelled at. Not even once. My sister and I were loved, and told we were loved unconditionally all the time.

None of this meant my parents knew what to do with me. I did not fit what the parenting books said should be working. My mom tells me now that there was a lot of trial and error and creativity with her parenting. She would try something. It would blow up in her face. She would conclude that it didn't work, and try something else. When a technique would work, she would remember and use it again.

I faced many routine issues common with kids on the autism spectrum.

My dad was not an athlete, but did dutifully try to teach me sports. He took me to games. I remember him teaching me to play catch in the front yard. Being afraid of the ball was not irrational in my world. More balls bounced off me than ever were caught. I think we both accepted sports were not my thing when I turned my baseball bat, not once used for baseball, into the clubhouse flagpole. That was okay. Sports weren't his thing either.

In many ways I was a clueless kid. In kindergarten several times a week all year long I would get off the bus, walk into the wrong room and start crying. I would also be known for missing the bus home for the first couple years of school. I'd find myself standing there alone as they all pulled away. Someone would eventually find me and take me to the office where they would call my mom. I had a habit of getting lost in stores too. Besides liking to go into the center of round clothing fixtures, deadening the sound (sensory), I liked the display of the dishwasher with the glass front, watching the water splash around (also sensory). Really, for much of early life I was in a fog.

As good as home was, school was bad. It was horrible. To this day, decades later, school is still one of a handful of recurring themes in my nightmares.

To begin with, my first grade teacher didn't understand me, who I was, or how I operated. As a result she became physically and verbally abusive. I was routinely grabbed, shaken, yelled at, and humiliated. I remember more than once being dragged (literally, not figuratively) to the nurse's office where the teacher would demand that the nurse tell her what was wrong with me.

I recall the beginning of the end. I had gotten an answer wrong that she concluded no one should get wrong. I had to sit on the floor in front of her desk until I got the answer right, while the other kids went on with their typical day. I sat there all day, with her rude comments. Finally I was shaken by the upper arm and harshly told the answer, as well as how stupid I was. The answer was that I was to have circled the picture of the cap. I didn't know the word "cap". I thought it was a hat, which clearly doesn't start with "C". I still have that assignment at home.

I recognize she was troubled, and as an adult I hold her no ill will. It would only hurt me. Enough people had seen her treatment of me over time, and shortly after this final episode she disappeared and I had a new teacher. Why didn't I tell someone? I lacked the ability to communicate those types of ideas and feelings. I didn't know how. Now as a professional, many decades later, I have walked into that same school building and been overwhelmed with feelings and memories that I thought had been under control for a long time. I guess some things are forever.

I had some excellent teachers through the years. That does not mean school, or my life at school, went well. My dysgraphia was and is severe.

Hanging in my office is a paper I remember doing. I was about nine years old. I was to copy a simple sentence from the board. It took me in excess of forty-five minutes, and what I wrote wasn't even close. In elementary school kids would tell me how to spell something, and they would give me a jumbled list of letters to see if I would believe them. I did. Throughout school my spelling test scores could have been tripled and still be a failing grade. I was unable to spell almost anything until halfway through college.

The ability to communicate academic knowledge was a challenge, and much of what I know now I taught myself as an adult. At one point in high school I had a midterm grade of 5 out of 120. Failing grades were common. My mom, who was an excellent student, jokes with me saying the only reason I'm still alive is my dad, who also struggled in school. He was able to explain my challenges to her. But he didn't like it either. He made that perfectly clear to me on many occasions. Still, he was able to understand.

As hard as academic subjects were for me, the non-academic subjects were worse. As an example, in gym class we would play American football. It was assumed growing up in the Buffalo, NY area that every boy knew the rules. I didn't. I could handle not getting thrown or handed the ball. I figured I'd live longer that way. But I didn't know the difference between a fumble and an incomplete pass. They were both on the ground. I would get yelled at for not diving on a fumble. I would get laughed at when I began diving on incomplete passes. No one ever explained the difference.

Kids made up new words to the songs in music class to humiliate me. When we would sing the songs in class they would sing their new revised version. They even wrote the modified words in the school music books. As far as I know nothing was ever done on my behalf. I never told anyone, but shouldn't have had to either.

Peer issues in school were worse than my academic challenges. I'll admit I was beyond a little different. To say that I was very unique compared to my peers, even odd, would be a polite way of putting it. I dressed different. I carried my books "like a girl". My shirt would be ripped open. My books would be knocked out of my hands and kicked down the hall. Lunch would be the worst part of my day as I was a completely defenseless sitting target. Not all kids were mean to me, but many were. Looking back now I know some kids tried to help me. At the time I lacked the ability to know the difference between the two types of kids, so simply being left alone and ignored was about as good as my life got through much of school.

My parents learned to go with my interests in life. Christmas and birthday gifts included: Legos, a microscope, chemistry set, telescope, coins, antiques, art supplies, and so on. I was exposed to wide-ranging beneficial interests. Things such as concerts, museums, antique shows, fancy restaurants, the theater, parks, and many church events were standard in my life.

It was actually church and the people there which rescued me. I was accepted there, and that became my social circle. I was actively involved. I was even given the chance for peer leadership there. Most importantly I was mentored by some excellent hand-picked people who made a huge difference in my life.

So, how did I get from a geeky clueless child with no foreseeable future to where I am now in life? The shift began at about age twelve.

I was not diagnosed with autism or anything else until I was in my late thirties. I was born in 1966, and at that time such diagnoses were not understood. At twelve my parents sat me down and said that they had seen all the specialists and done all the testing that they knew how. They knew something was "wrong", but didn't know what. They promised to love me, and help me any way they could, but whether or not I made it in life was up to me and the decisions I made.

At that moment I began to put together a plan. I set for myself major life goals and, as much as a twelve-year-old is capable, planned out the rest of my life, and how I was going to go about it. The specifics for my life plan have changed many times. However, even after all these decades, the basic goals haven't changed. My top goal was to make a difference in the world. While it may sound youthfully simplistic and idealistic, it has remained my primary goal to this day.

Soon after that conversation at twelve years old I would come home from school and study. I wasn't studying any academics, but studying about life. My mom was a therapist, and I would go into her library and study psychology, counseling, and any self-help book or book about people I could get my hands on. I identified patterns and ranges of what was typical and expected interpersonal behavior, and began to implement changes in my life to parallel what I was learning. My study also helped me figure out other people, their emotions, intentions, and behaviors. Some of the techniques I discuss in this book are things I began to develop many decades ago as a kid. They were autism-based and worked.

There were many pivotal choices and moments throughout my teens and early adult life. Some I have shared at various points in my writing. I will also share a handful here for background.

My parents never told me I couldn't do or accomplish something I wanted. I was raised to be fiercely independent and a calculated risk taker. At age fifteen I went and did lifeguard training because my church friends did it. I couldn't swim. No surprise I failed the course, but it taught me to swim. The next year I did it again and aced the course. On a different occasion, two weeks after being bedridden for weeks with pneumonia, I joined my church friends on a hundred-mile one-day bike trip through the mountains. I wasn't particularly gifted on a bike when healthy. It wasn't pretty, but I made it.

In college I took argumentation and debate. It was likely my most valuable course. I didn't get good marks, but it taught me how to think on my feet. Likewise living overseas exposed me to the study of cultural anthropology which has helped immensely.

My degree was in Bible, minoring in Christian Education. Straight out of college I was fired from two jobs in the ministry. I discovered that I did not have the bureaucratic, political, or interpersonal skills to survive as a professional in the North American church. I spent the next five years delivering pizzas for a living. This was one of the most valuable times of my life. I learned how to live in poverty. I learned to deal with my pride and judgmental attitude towards others, and how to separate a person's worth from their bad decisions.

In my thirties I took in a teen who needed a place to go, and raised him as if he were my own. Present in him were autism and other developmental issues, mental health struggles, and severe learning disabilities. He lived with me six years. I am not going to share much for the sake of his privacy. Suffice to say I can now understand where many parents are coming from in ways I could not before. (He is now an adult, living on his own, and doing well.)

My life and the world around me finally began to make sense for the first time in my late thirties when I was diagnosed as being on the autism spectrum. I used to wonder things such as whether I was hard working or lazy. I cared about others and tried to say the right things, but would still end up hurting feelings. Was I intelligent or stupid? There were finally answers and a sense of relief.

Through the decades of figuring things out, and having worked with kids in various capacities since 1985, I realized I had a valuable skillset in the area of autism that fit with my life goals and dreams. After a few years' planning, in 2011 I walked away from corporate America with its steady salary, benefits package, and company car. I started my own business, "CNY Autism Consulting".

I currently spend half my time working with people in a clinical office setting as a consultant, and half my time doing field work mentoring two autistic brothers. I go to their home, bring them into my home, and also take them out into the community. I like the mix of both clinical and field work. I also do school observations, public speaking, have run a support group, advise and serve on boards, and am involved in many other ways in serving the autism community. I tell people I do essentially anything that can be imagined in the autism world except prescribe meds. (I'm not a doctor.)

I know what I know not through formal education, but through life. I have a bachelor's degree, with an unimpressive grade point average, in an unrelated field, in a business dominated by people with doctorate degrees. That being said, I have an amazing track record of helping people accomplish the impossible. If fancy degrees and a bunch of letters after a name mean a lot to you, I'm likely not your person. If you are primarily interested in results and success, give me and what I have to say a try.

I tell those who come to me that I am different than anyone they have worked with before. I am not a therapist, and I don't work like a therapist, developmental specialist, behavior specialist, or any of the other common professionals in the autism world. I'm more like an engineer. I know what makes autism like it is. I know how to take what is present in a person's life, piece it together, and make it work. It is not making the autistic person the same as everyone else, or using methodologies that work for non-autistic people. I want to help someone be fully successful at being who they are, autism and all, and live successfully in a world not set up for autism.

I often have parents tell me that they want my life for their child. I get it. I am independent, successful, self-employed, and so on. It is a compliment, and I take it as such. It is a sign they have hope. However, I tell them I don't want my life for their child. My life is full of trauma and baggage that has helped make me who I am, but will be there forever. I tell them my goal for their child is that they learn from me, what I have figured out the hard way, and by using that information they can be more successful than I have been. Many have done so, and more are well on their way.

PART A

LIFE WITH AUTISM

1. PET THE CAT

Most of those who come into my office do so because life is not going well. There is emotional upset and/or behavioral issues in life. One of the first things I try to do is determine if these issues are a part of who the person is, or as a result of what a professional would call the "environment". This has nothing to do with the weather, but is referring to the things going on in that person's life around them.

The most common thing I see with autism is anxiety. Life is not kind to those who are autistic. We are living in a world not set up for autism. The way those on the spectrum describe life is typically as overwhelming and confusing. The culture or operating system of autism is distinctly different from people in the general population. What may make things better for someone not autistic can make things worse for those on the spectrum. Typically those involved are not trying to be malicious, but trying to help. The problem is they don't know the proper approach because autistic people are wired differently. It creates the type of situation I refer to as petting a cat.

Think of those of us who are autistic as like a cat. If you pet a cat the way the fur lies, you will have a happy pleasant kitty that will purr, snuggle, and do well. If you pet the cat against the fur ... not so much. You will get clawed, bitten, and if it happens to the cat often enough it will run to avoid you at all costs. Observers would find your behavior abusive, and scold you for torturing the cat. You'd have a cat with emotional difficulties. Not because the cat was wired that way to begin with, but because the poor thing reached the point it just couldn't take it anymore.

Others do this all the time with those of us who are on the autism spectrum. We are always being "pet against the fur". And then an expert comes along with therapies to help us deal with the anxiety that comes from being pet against the fur. Few seem to understand the concept that at the core we are different, and our fur lies in a different direction.

Clearly this harm is not intentional. Helping someone who is autistic can be counter-intuitive, where doing what would help most people can make things worse with autism. People have often figured out what will not work. However, most are at a loss about what will work.

There are answers. A lot of what I do professionally is to teach autistic kids, their parents, and others what direction the fur lies with autism, and to help them pet the cat the right way. Once this happens, improvement is often quick, dramatic, and everyone wins. We then have a happy kitty.

That is much of what this book is about. Demystifying autism and helping others understand what will work with those on the autism spectrum. It is building bridges and understanding between the non-autism and autism worlds.

Unfortunately being pet against the fur is a reality of life with autism. It will never be completely eliminated. There will always be some who do not understand autism, whether they are incapable of understanding or simply choose not to.

The world needs to be presented the way it really is to those on the spectrum, not as we would like it to be, or the way it should be. However, by understanding the differences that come with autism we can make things better for those on the autism spectrum. While it may be naïve of me, I truly believe most people in the world want to get things right, and any errors are due to ignorance. By helping others understand what direction the fur lies on the autism kitty, autistic people's lives can be more successful.

2. BEHAVIOR AS COMMUNICATION

Part of what brings people into my office is parents' concern about the behaviors of their autistic kids. Something is wrong and they want it to change. One of my goals in working with the family is to help them understand that behavior is communication. Their child is telling them something. The challenge is to decode it.

With autism there are multiple barriers to effective communication, even for those who are older and/or fully verbal. The breakdown in effective communication is one aspect of what makes autism what it is. It is part of the diagnostic criteria.

Due to these communication struggles, there are times when communication is happening but most people around are unaware. The kid does something inappropriate. Someone else reacts to the inappropriate action. That reaction is read by the child. The two have just communicated. When looking to connect with others, and not being good at it, a child can inadvertently behave inappropriately because it is a form of communication and they want to connect. At times it can be this simple.

If this is a part of what is happening, then ignoring the unwanted behavior, while going to extreme measures to connect with the child when behaving appropriately, is a part of the solution. But this solution does come with a caution: the extinction curve.

Behavior serves a purpose. It is meeting a need. If the behavior does not accomplish anything then it would not exist (though there are occasions a behavior originally met a purpose, but then takes on a life of its own even after the original purpose ceases to exist). When a behavior that was meeting a need no longer meets that need – when the behavior is ignored – the child will try twice as hard for twice as long to try to get the expected result. If after escalation happens the adult ultimately gives in, all that has happened is that the line has moved within the child regarding intensity. The unwanted behavior is now going to be worse rather than better.

Parents need to be aware of this escalation within the extinction curve. Do not begin to try this if unusually exhausted and stressed, because things will get worse before they get better. Enough emotional and physical energy is needed to survive the escalation that will be there prior to the behavior dying off.

My mom tells about one experience when I was about two. I threw my temper tantrum and she simply walked out of the room with absolutely no reaction. I concluded that it didn't work and dropped it from my repertoire. I am not foolish enough to think this experience is typical.

One thing I will always give my parents credit for is that they never let me get away with anything. Absolutely nothing. If the battle lines were drawn, they won every time, no matter what. I too have tried to model this with kids. I do not need to fight a battle, and if I see a battle coming I have the option of stepping aside and letting it go right on by. However, once battle lines are drawn, and it is a win/lose scenario, as the adult I must win absolutely every single time, and so should you.

Over years I mastered the art of seeing battles coming and leaving myself an out. "Would you mind emptying the dishwasher sometime in the next couple hours?" What is my out? In this example it is the "Would you mind". If I am met with an explosive surly monster my reply would be something like: "Well, I didn't demand you do it, I asked if you would mind. Clearly there is a problem. Can we talk about it?" This is different than if I demanded the dishwasher be emptied. If it was an order, I have lost flexibility and need to win the battle over the dishwasher: something that ultimately isn't very important.

I remember once telling a kid whose diagnostic mix included OCD to pick up something they considered dirty and contaminated. You would have thought I had told them to carve their heart out with a soup spoon. I had yelling, screaming, threat making, flailing, all inches in front of my face. Though I could have solved the immediate problem in seconds by picking it up myself, the reality was I was stuck. The battle lines were drawn, and as the adult I needed to win. It took over an hour, but with the help of surgical gloves, kitchen tongs, and a plastic bag, the dirty item was able to be picked up. Though a miserable experience for all, it was the first and last time. That kid knew if I made a demand, I would win no matter how long or miserable the fight. While I worked to keep the demands down, they were always followed, and there was never a repeat. The kid knew I was serious.

There is also the art of negotiation. I truly believe most behavior is designed to meet a need, whether that need is direct communication itself, or something more tangible. It does not take a genius to figure out that if a kid is throwing a fit about going to school (complete with yelling, kicking, throwing things, and so on), there is a problem with going to school – not unusual with autism, as is the need for occasional days off. My solution for having to win battles, but also recognizing legitimate needs, is negotiation.

"If you behave inappropriately, including: yelling, kicking, throwing [and whatever else the list needs to be] then I am stuck. If I give in to inappropriate behavior that makes me a bad parent/adult, and I am not going to do that. One way or the other, your butt is going out that door. However, if you can calmly and appropriately explain to me that you are overwhelmed, tired, or whatever else, and would like to stay home, that at least gives me options. There are times I too am overwhelmed, or exhausted, and can't face my day. I cancel everything and spend the day doing nothing. It is a part of life with autism. If it is reasonable for me, it is reasonable for you too, as long as it doesn't happen too often. Let's also figure out why school is a problem and what changes we can make to help you be more successful there. I want to give you what you need, but you need to work with me." This approach has always served me well.

One other thing I try to do is put myself in their place. If I were in their shoes, would I consider the request reasonable and legitimate? Somehow we see things as more legitimate when coming from another adult, but it should not matter if it is an adult or a child making the request. If we see behavior as communication, and work backwards from the behavior to determine the need being met, we can then help the person meet their needs in a more appropriate and successful way.

Sometimes it can be a challenge to determine what the message or cause of a behavior is. For example, a child hitting themselves in the head, or head banging – it is not clear what the message is. Sinus infection or other pain? Seeking sensory input? Self-blaming for lack of perfection? Emotional disturbance? I have seen all of these, and it can take some thought and digging to get the right answer, typically through experimentation and a process of elimination.

I was once on vacation and met a woman with her six-year-old son who was under treatment for being emotionally disturbed, and was prone to frequent violent outbursts. As I was interacting with both of them, and she was picking my brain, she and I both concluded fairly quickly that autism was a factor in her son's life. One of the conversations I had with them during my vacation was about the sensory needs that exist with autism, including deep pressure. The boy heard this. The next morning her son came to her and said: "Mommy, hold me like I hit you." He was using violent outbursts as the only method he knew to get deep pressure, by being restrained. Within a couple weeks of starting sensory work, especially deep pressure, the outbursts dramatically tapered off, and within months had gone away. The child was an autistic extreme sensory seeker and no one knew it. He was communicating in the only way he knew how: through his behavior.

We also want to make sure we are solving the right issue. It can be more complicated. I had a girl I worked with who liked to play board games, and every time she did not win she would throw the game at my head. Some would say she needs to win. While it is true that with autism we do not like to lose, it is equally true you can't always win in the real world. So is the issue that she must learn how to lose? I would say partially, but what appears to be the issue is sometimes a symptom of what is deeper. There was a deeper need for: confidence, self-image, the ability to anticipate the unexpected or undesired results, emotional stability, and emotional connection to others. As those were accomplished her ability to gracefully handle many difficult life situations, including losing, flourished. I always try to get back to the root cause of an issue and not merely deal with the symptom presenting itself. While the problem was at a more complicated deeper level, her behavior was still communication.

There can be many different drivers to behavior, including behaviors driven by some mental health issues, all of which need differing types of interventions. This can change the motivating factors behind a behavior. Some of what I do as a professional is to help determine if something is being driven by issues other than autism or normal life factors. Such things could be: depression, anxiety, mood disorders, OCD, psychosis, personality disorders, dissociative disorders, or even anti-social disorders such as psychopathy or sociopathy. Even when these differing causations and motivations are in play, behavior serves as communication. It is a symptom of a much larger issue than the presenting behavior itself.

While we have discussed techniques such as negotiation here to resolve need-driven behavior, this is not a chapter on discipline. For advice pertaining to disciplinary issues, please see chapter thirty-two.

3. ANXIETY

*"I don't want to go to sleep because each day is a day
closer to death and I don't want to die."*
- Autistic five-year-old boy

Every minute of every day most of those on the autism spectrum live
with levels of anxiety that would absolutely crush the majority of non-
autistic people and leave them a whimpering blob of goop on the floor.
It is our normal ... all day every day. It literally influences every decision
made and invades everything in life. Anxiety is so common with autism
that I always presume it is there, and find it atypical if it is not. People
on the spectrum are able to function because they have never known
anything else.

It's not one single thing that causes anxiety, but the cumulative impact
over time of trying to function in a world not set up for autism. We can
only handle so much stress and agitation before there are significant

problems. It is like trying to put ten pounds of manure into a five pound bag. It just can't be done, and there will be a mess made in the process.

I know one mother of an autistic boy who describes the anxiety in her son as like filling a pitcher of water. At the start of a normal day his pitcher is already fifty percent full. This is just the base agitation of being autistic and trying to function in an unfriendly world. No matter what, this is as good as it gets, and the anxiety pitcher is never empty. You would never know there is a problem because there is no mess, but there is still water there. Then if there is something that bothers him, perhaps an itchy shirt, that might add another thirty percent to his pitcher, bringing him up to eighty percent. Still no mess, but getting closer. Add another thing that bothers him, such as sinus pressure, or trying to cut with scissors, or a change in the television schedule, and another thirty percent is added to the already eighty percent full pitcher. At this point there is overflow and meltdown. The goal is to keep the pitcher as empty as possible so that overflow is less likely.

After an in-depth conversation about anxiety and autism I have had people ask: "How do those on the autism spectrum function?" "With these levels of anxiety how does someone even get out of bed in the morning and face the world?" My response is that by understanding enough to ask that question they are now at the very earliest stages of grasping what life with autism is like. The truth is, a lot of the time those on the spectrum don't function well.

It is not unusual for our autistic kids to have days when they can't go to school. The anxiety has reached the point of overload. They just can't. I do the same thing. Some days when I get up I know my day is already over. I cancel everything except clients in crisis. There are those who joke about taking "mental health days". Those on the spectrum really do.

We may all from time to time want to run yelling from the room. I know an autistic nine-year-old who does so on a regular basis. He will reach the point where he just can't take it anymore. You will hear a primal scream followed by the pitter patter of little feet.

The anxieties don't need to be even remotely rational. I know of one kid who is petrified of hurricanes. He would not go outside in a slight breeze. Instead he would hide under a table. While this might make sense living in coastal Florida, he lives in upstate New York. Blizzards, yes. Hurricanes, no. One time he passed out because he decided to hold his breath to try and achieve a sense of control.

Is anxiety the same as autism? No. However, I wanted to mention it because it is such a common issue with those on the autism spectrum that it is nearly universal. The good news is that – in my experience – as someone develops a better understanding of their own autism, and those around them also develop understanding and learn how to provide support, anxiety levels can be lowered to manageable functional levels. It will still be there, but it can be lived with.

4. INTENT

"I'm a good boy. I haven't bit you yet."
- Autistic child to dentist

I often ask autistic kids if there was only one thing they could have people understand about them and their autism what it would be. The answer is almost universal. Good intent. People presume motives that are not accurate, and almost always negative.

Life on the autism spectrum is hard enough without being wrongly blamed for having bad intent when things go wrong. They are accused of being: manipulative, demanding, self-centered, lazy, controlling, uncaring, sneaky, a jerk, or a variety of other words not fit to print.

It is doubly painful when it comes from people who should know better. Those who should understand and be there to help, but instead often presume guilty until proven innocent. I am advised: "While they are autistic, they are still kids, and will try to pull typical kid stuff.

When they do, they need to be treated like all other kids." While there are exceptions, as a general rule this is wrong with autism.

Situations where it may be simple to determine intent with a typical kid are not so simple with autism. By diagnostic definition those on the autism spectrum lack the ability to read other people, as well as social or life situations. An experienced person on the autism spectrum can learn how to fake it, or give intellectually appropriate responses. However, for someone younger or inexperienced to do it in real life, in real time, with real people? Nope! They just can't. Diagnostically impossible.

Behavior that appears openly defiant, manipulative, presumptuous, and/or insensitive generally isn't with autism. It seems like they are purposefully being a jerk, and at the outward observable level they are accomplishing being a jerk beautifully. However, that is not their intent.

I know some will think I am being a fool, and have no child-rearing sense whatsoever. Yes, I know … "Kids need to know who is in charge and stop trying to call the shots." Autism is different. What appears blatantly defiant likely isn't.

There are only two groups of autistic kids that I see routinely showing manipulative, deceitful behavior with ill intent. The first is when there is another mental health diagnosis in play with diagnostic characteristics of manipulation and deceit, such as borderline personality disorder, or someone who is a sociopath. The traits of the other diagnosis can wash out some of the elements of autism. The second group is an autistic child who was trying to survive in an abusive or neglectful situation, where they had to learn things such as manipulation and deceit to survive.

A slight caveat is what I will call misguided justice. This can happen a lot. These kids are perceiving themselves or others as having been wronged, and then responding inappropriately. While this is inappropriate behavior, it is not manipulation or deceit. It is seeking justice in the face of perceived wrongs. The problem is, even if they or someone else actually have been wronged, they are responding inappropriately.

More so than any group of people I can think of, those on the autism spectrum do what they do with good intent. Far more so than the general population. What is done by the person on the spectrum may not work well in life, and be inappropriate, but that doesn't mean the intent behind it is evil.

Now compare this with how often the autistic child is blamed. I have caught myself doing it. Something can sometimes appear so blatant, especially after the issue has been worked on and talked about for weeks or even months. But in these times I was wrong. Every single time I have dug into it the intent was not bad, and causation was something tied into the autism; no matter how clearly it appeared to be something else.

Most know that with autism there is a significant lack of social, cultural, and interpersonal skills. There is not the ability to effectively understand people, and why they do what they do. If things are a problem with a kid on the autism spectrum it is almost always for one of three reasons:

1. They don't know what to do. By diagnostic definition autism comes with interpersonal and social cluelessness. Even when an issue has been talked about does not mean the person on the autism spectrum knows what to do. With autism, life is full of overwhelming differences and variations, with an inability to tell what differences matter and what do not. The situational discernment filter most people operate with is missing with autism. Unless an instance is exactly, and I do mean exactly, like the one before, it can be interpreted as completely different, leaving the person on the spectrum legitimately clueless on what to do.

2. They don't know how to do it. Knowing at an intellectual level the correct social protocol of what do to, and the actual ability to do it in real time, with real people, in a nuanced real world situation, are completely different. We can know to not be rude. How to apply that in real life with competing value judgments and social complexities can be difficult. There are also hundreds if not thousands of these social rules. What may be obviously clear to the rest of the world isn't with autism.

3. They are completely tapped out, and have nothing left in the tank to do it with. Life with autism is hard, and it is not unusual to lack the emotional reserves needed to function. When operating in real life, facing the hardships of a world not set up for autism, a person can be at the point of marginal functioning, and unable to navigate within the rules of social nicety. They are in survival mode, just hanging on to the fringes of stability. They know how to do it. They just can't.

The lesson? Presuming only autism is a factor, unless painfully clear, as in they told you in simple unwavering terms that their intent was bad, and didn't change when questioned, presume that intent is good with autism. Yes, with autism we can be that clueless, stupid, and socially awkward. Most people understand how the world works – we don't. Honestly, to be manipulative and deceitful requires a social understanding and interpersonal skills people with autism generally don't have. If we did, we would not be on the autism spectrum. The diagnostic criteria would not be met. Extend the courtesy of presuming innocent until proven guilty, regardless of what the evidence may suggest.

5. HIGH AND LOW FUNCTIONING

We often hear the terms "high functioning" and "low functioning" used in the autism world. While I am not happy about it, and will usually qualify myself, I even find myself using the terms. What does high or low functioning really mean?

If an autistic child is non-verbal, toe walks, rocks and flaps, and makes no eye contact, are they high or low functioning? Truthfully, we don't have enough information. They may communicate effectively in ways other than verbally, have good academic achievement, be emotionally stable, be accepted by others, and generally be doing well.

If an autistic child is verbally articulate, is able to control repetitive behavior in public, and has learned to make good eye contact, are they high or low functioning? Again, we do not have enough information. They may have extra rigid thinking patterns, struggle to function in a school or home environment, have emotional stability challenges, be picked on by others, and not be doing well in life.

People are individuals. I know of a college professor who is highly respected around the world in his field. He is provided an aide by the university. However, the aide is not there to help him with his work. The aide makes sure he is dressed appropriately, eats when he needs to, and shows up to teach on time. Is the professor high functioning or low functioning?

With autism, what is meant by high functioning or low functioning? In most Western cultures it often comes down to speech. How well the person uses verbal spoken language. There is a presumption that if someone is not verbal then they are not capable, are severely disabled, incompetent, and low functioning. This is also true if someone is struggling academically. Conversely, if someone is verbal, especially articulate, and doing well academically, then they are seen as having good capabilities, great potential, and being high functioning. Neither is necessarily true.

"He is a little autistic." "There is a little autism in all of us." "They have mild autism." "His autism is severe." "They are disabled due to autism." "He will never make it in life due to autism." These types of phrases are often meant to be supportive or collaborative. I don't take them that way. They are not accurate and are harmful. Those who are high functioning face greater challenges than most realize. Those who are low functioning are capable of more than most realize. The truth is complex. We have created this unfortunate dichotomy in the autism world that some kids are high functioning and some kids are low functioning, and that the term "autism spectrum" refers to a range of functioning levels. I don't like it. It is wrong.

We use the same criteria to diagnose everyone on the autism spectrum. Autistic is autistic. Either we are, or we are not. It is the same operating system. Instead of a high to low functioning, the term "autism spectrum" refers to a variety of manifestations of the same struggles.

Most would consider me high functioning. I own my own home, have no debt, am self-employed, and sit on professional committees. While I think little about speaking in front of hundreds of people, I have spent decades developing the skills to do so easily. It is the quiet and private areas of life at home where I struggle. Paying bills, getting out of bed in the morning, maintaining my home. Mostly, the incredible amount of down time I require to function at the levels I do. I require ten or more hours of sleep a night. I additionally need several hours of quiet and private time each day. I perform at an extremely high level when I need to, but that comes at what many non-autistic people would see as a huge cost. People identify me as "high functioning". What I think, but don't usually say, is: "Sometimes."

I know a teen many would describe as low functioning. For example, he needs help dressing, would be classified as non-verbal or semi-verbal, and can't do basic math. However, socially this kid is far more popular than I have ever been. He is also emotionally stable, confident and comfortable in who he is. He has an energy and drive I could only dream about. This "low functioning" kid has areas of his life that are ahead of most others on the spectrum.

Instead of viewing the autism spectrum as a continuum of high to low functioning, I describe it as more like a professional sound board. On a sound board each slider, dial, and knob represents different frequencies. Any one of these could be in a high, medium, or low position, and chances are there will be some of each.

With autism, each slider, dial, and knob represents an issue that someone with autism has in their life. Each of these issues can be in a high, medium, or low position. In every autistic individual there will be some of each. Different individual mixes can contribute to differing looks, but the range of common issues is universally present. Don't view any person as overall "high functioning" or "low functioning", or "severely autistic" as opposed to "less autistic". Look at how each individual is coping with each area of their life, and their own unique mix of strengths and weaknesses. See a person. Don't make presumptions. Get to know them for who they really are.

6. DON'T BLAME AUTISM

If you could get rid of autism, would you?

Some view those on the autism spectrum as a burden on society or to families. I had one parent claim high levels of socialization had been necessary for the creation of civilization and human success. I disagreed. Those on the autism spectrum communicate, socialize, and are productive, though through a different set of social rules. Society would be different, but would work just fine if autism-based. Most who are not on the autism spectrum would find an autism-based culture difficult. I assure you those on the autism spectrum currently find non-autism-based society equally difficult.

As a culture we are good at putting out a public message of acceptance. We have bumper stickers, shirts, walks, and other feel good stuff. However I on occasion encounter anger, lack of understanding, denial, intolerance, arrogance, embarrassment, and a lot more. I at times have heard people say they hate autism. Literally, "I hate autism." And it is often not strangers, but those in an autistic person's inner circle saying it.

We often blame autism for things that have nothing to do with autism. I understand people hating some of the things that often accompany autism, such as: limited expressive verbal speech (verbal apraxia), toileting delays, physical clumsiness, intellectual disability, anxiety, depression, emotional upset, obsessive compulsive disorder, and all the other accompanying diagnoses. However, this is not autism. Do not blame the autism.

Autism is lack of interpersonal skill. Not being good at the back and forth interaction between people. Struggling to read others, or have them read us. Relationships are different than expected, or even missing. We struggle to understand the culture around us. We have special interests (often called obsessions by the non-autism world). We like structure, routine, and predictability, and there is sensory seeking and/or avoidance.

Where do the accompanying issues people hate come from? Typically from a separate diagnosis and/or the hardships of life living in a world not set up for autism.

Having coexisting mental health and/or physical diagnoses is very common with autism. If someone also has cerebral palsy, Ehlers-Danlos syndrome, or is visually impaired, no one blames those problems on autism. It is understood these diagnoses exist alongside the autism. The same should be said for verbal apraxia, dyspraxia, gastrointestinal issues, or learning disabilities. It should also be true for mental health problems such as anxiety, depression, OCD, or mood disorders. They are there alongside the autism. Blame those diagnoses for their own problems, not the autism.

There are struggles associated with autism that come from the hardships of trying to function in a world that is not autism-friendly, and the resulting damage. If the world ran the way those of us on the autism spectrum would like, we would be fine. Everyone else would be in therapy. Because we are in the minority we must learn to adapt, and often are misunderstood. It is what I have described as petting a cat against the fur in chapter one. The results can be anxiety, depression, and trauma. I see it a lot. These are almost universal above a certain age. This is not autism itself, but a result of lack of understanding.

Whether as a result of a coexisting diagnosis along with the autism, or as a result of trying to live in a world not set up for those on the spectrum, I encourage people to put blame where it belongs. Target the frustration and hate at these issues. Not the autism. Autism didn't cause them. Remember what autism is. Autism is interpersonal difficulties, social cluelessness, thriving in predictable environments, special interests, and sensory struggles. That "other stuff" is not autism.

Before we say we hate autism we need to check to see if it is really the autism we hate. I like my autism. I do not like my anxiety, learning disabilities, or trauma history. If it is truly the autism you hate, then I'm sorry. In the world at large I personally do not encounter that many actual autism acceptance problems. Only issues of ignorance. I can fix ignorance with education.

Experience has taught me that those on the spectrum who are in an environment where they are understood and appreciated for who they are typically thrive, and can function in a world not set up for autism. We live life differently, but successfully. Is everything about autism and those on the autism spectrum wonderful and perfect? Of course not. But many parts of the non-autistic world and culture have serious issues too.

7. VIEW FROM INSIDE AUTISM

"βλεπομεν γαρ αρτι δι εσοπτρου εν αινιγματι ..."
"For now we see through a glass darkly ..."
- I Corinthians 13:12a

People ask me what it feels like to be autistic. The simplest answer I can give is that being autistic is feeling a little overwhelmed and confused all the time. That is because when we step out of our front door we are walking into a culture not our own.

Imagine you are on an exotic vacation. You have no idea where. You also had no idea you were going. You just wake up one morning in this strange land, all alone. If you prefer, consider yourself kidnapped, or abducted by aliens. Things are familiar, but wrong. It is as if you woke up in some strange movie. Everyone seems to know you, and assume you know what is going on. You are confused and overwhelmed. Being intelligent, competent, and out of options, you decide to make the best of it.

You quickly learn that making the best of it is not as easy as it sounds. The language is English, but people keep misunderstanding what you are saying, and getting upset in the process. You find a lot of the food unpalatable. Some parts of this world are too bright, while others are too dark. There are wild temperature fluctuations and you always seem too cold or too hot. You start to notice that everyone is treating you differently. There are complex social rules that you can't figure out and people are getting impatient with you. These are things you are expected to know. Everyone else knows this stuff, and can't figure out what is wrong with you. You try to ask for help to learn these bizarre rules, but no one seems to understand your pleas. You know it isn't going well. You have no idea why. You observe and try to mimic what is going on around you, but no one seems to appreciate your efforts to fit in. You are not feeling so intelligent and competent anymore. Don't worry, you get to wake up tomorrow and do the same thing all over again, and continue doing so for the rest of your life. And let's not forget, the complex rules of this strange new world are constantly evolving, seeming to change almost daily.

Does this scenario sound like a great adventure, or more like a nightmare? Obviously I am describing only a little piece of what it is like to be on the autism spectrum, trying to function in the non-autistic world. Is it really this bad? It can be.

As mentioned earlier, in middle school while playing gym class football I didn't know the difference between a fumble and an incomplete pass. No one taught me. Growing up in Buffalo, NY it was considered impossible for a boy to reach that age and not know basic rules of American football. It may seem inconsequential and unimportant, until you are that kid who is the only one on the field that has absolutely no idea what is going on. I would have a fumbled football lying at my feet and get yelled at for ignoring it. Just when I thought I had it figured out (the ball was on the ground) I started diving on incomplete passes. They weren't yelling anymore, but they were laughing. No one explained the differences to me in a way I could understand. I wanted to do the right thing, but I didn't know how. If this were just an isolated instance, no big deal. It wasn't. It was one of thousands. It is an all-day every-day experience for those of us who are on the autism spectrum. We are perpetually a little lost and confused.

There are multiple factors in these struggles. There is: executive functioning, sensory issues, anxiety, overwhelming options, perfectionism, cultural breakdown, priority conflicts, communication problems, learning disabilities, and more. It may take time to figure out the problem or combination of problems.

The individual mix of reasons for not knowing what to do is slightly different with each person and situation. We are all individuals with differing backgrounds. But the one thing all of us with autism have in common is that we are all a little lost and confused. We are in a perpetual fog when it comes to things outside our areas of expertise. What often confuses people is our mix of struggles combined with areas of great accomplishment. I hear variations of this theme all the time. "Why can my child be a chess master, or know everything there is to know about trains, but can't figure out how to use silverware?"

In the autistic world that I live and work in, that type of mix is common, and makes complete sense. We are typically skilled at things most others find a challenge, while we struggle with the areas of life most take for granted and view as simple. With autism we are in a minority, we don't get to pick the social rules, and we must learn to function in a world not set up for autism.

8. NEURO-TYPICAL DISORDER

What if those on the autism spectrum were not the minority, and in a position to make the rules about how the world worked? Here is how the diagnostic criteria might look if things were reversed, mirroring the DSM-5 criteria for autism spectrum disorder. Instead of "autism spectrum disorder" I bring you "neuro-typical disorder" ("neuro-typical" is a common phrase to describe those not on the autism spectrum). The goal is not to be critical of the world, but to offer a new perspective.

Neuro-Typical Disorder

1) Persistent excess in social communication and social interaction across multiple contexts, as manifested by the following, currently or by history (examples are illustrative, not exhaustive):

   a) Excessive social-emotional reciprocity and communication ranging, for example, from the expectation that others talk about and participate in their interests, to excessively expressing and sharing of emotions, or the expectation of back and forth communication about trivial items. May struggle with being specific or completely truthful in communication, valuing emotions or feelings over truth.

b) Deficits in non-verbal communicative behaviors used for social interaction, ranging for example, from unreadable facial expressions, body language, and vocal tones. May claim clear communication with these non-verbal elements, but lacking in skill to communicate beyond extreme positive or negative expressions. May persist in attempts to make eye contact. These unspoken and often unseen elements of expression may be claimed to negate the otherwise clear message of spoken words, resulting in lack of clarity or untruthfulness.

c) Excessive dependence on other people and relationships, ranging, for example, from an expectation of multiple connections with multiple people, to such connections taking priority over other areas of life. May claim interpersonal interaction is relaxing. Play can have the expectation of being interactive, without scientific or experimental purpose, and may be overly social. Likely prefers friends of same age, gender, and culture.

2) Excessively flexible or undirected and random behavior, interests, or activities, as manifested by at least two of the following, currently or by history (examples are illustrative, not exhaustive):

a) Lack of repetitive motor movements, use of objects, or speech. (Example: absence of flapping, rocking, bouncing or other movements used for self-regulation. Toys or other object will be placed without reason or order. Speech and word selection may be random and not based on previously tried and proven phrases.)

b) Lack of routine or pattern of verbal or non-verbal behavior. (Example: everyday life decisions are seemingly random rather than based on routines established in reason or efficiency. Difficulty focusing thought, and will move seamlessly from activity to activity. Lack of desired perfection in decision-making and actions, claiming there can be more than one right way, or more than one best food or toy.)

c) Lack of area of specialization or expertise. May claim multiple areas in life hold interest, and no single one is significantly more important or holds special value. May have a hobby which can mimic such specialization or expertise, but lacks the depth and focus for true proficiency. (Example: may claim to have an interest in cars, but is unable to identify them based solely on headlights. Will claim to have many interests such as Legos, stuffed animals, cooking, and more, but none is clearly superior, and other elements of life, such as sleep, food, or safety, can interfere and take precedence.)

d) Lack of acuity to the sensory world, or lack of awareness or connection with sensory aspects of the environment. (Example: is not bothered by what would bother a typical person, while also not experiencing the same level of joy or appreciation of elements of the sensory world. Neither seeking nor avoiding sensory experiences, as if numb or out of touch with the physical world around them. Lack of awareness of sounds, smells, texture, and other sensory experience. Unlikely to be able to identify others by scent, hear own heartbeat, or distinguish all ingredients in a food by taste.)

3) Symptoms must be present in the early developmental period. (May be masked by learned strategies in later life.)

4) Symptoms cause clinically significant impairment in social, occupational, or other important areas of current functioning.

5) These disturbances are not better explained by intellectual disability, traumatic brain injury, or mental health diagnoses.

9. RELATIONSHIPS

I held a sobbing autistic eight year old in my office. He wanted a friend. Any friend. It did not matter who they were. Everyone around him had friends, and all he wanted was one friend. Anyone. He didn't want to be so alone.

With autism we have a hard time with interpersonal relationships. It is a part of the diagnosis. This difficulty is not due to lack of desire or need, but lack of skill and proficiency. We have a hard time connecting and relating to people, which makes friendships difficult to start. We unintentionally damage relationships, making friendships hard to keep.

None of this eliminates the need for connecting with other people. It only makes it hard to meet that need. It also means every person who is in the life of someone on the spectrum is so much more important to the autistic child, teen, or adult than they would be to most other people.

I painted a painting as a teen. In it there are two people sitting by a fire with woods in the background and a great expanse of darkness surrounding them. The painting represents the importance people have to each other in the world. There is the warm glow of the fire and companionship, with the great mysterious and scary unknown floating just outside the pocket of safety. I am one of those two by the fire. Take away the other person and it would give the painting a whole different feel. We would be left with loneliness and isolation. Even fear. Instead we have comfort, peace, joy, warmth, security.

When I painted this painting I had many struggles in the world, but no diagnosis. While I knew the painting reflected an aspect of my experience with the world, it is only now, decades later, with a diagnosis in place, that I fully appreciate what I had painted.

With autism, the people in our lives matter. We cannot handle relationships with the same number of people that most can, and would find it overwhelming if we tried. But the need for connection with others is no less. Because there are so few people in our lives, each person matters to a greater degree than they might to most, and they cannot be easily replaced.

It might surprise you to find that many with autism spend significantly more thought, time, and energy working on relationships with others than most non-autistic people. We have to. It does not come naturally and requires huge amounts of work. It may not show on the observable outside as we interact with others, but that huge amount of work and focus is typically there.

Think about a person after a debilitating injury that has to spend months or years learning to walk again. That person will devote a huge portion of their day and energy to the goal of getting up and taking that next step. They may never have the same ability they used to. However they will do the best they can with what they have. For them to walk with a limp takes more focus and struggle than a typical person who walks perfectly. That person will also never again in their life take the ability to walk or run for granted. They will cherish every step.

The same is true for those of us with autism, and the people in our lives. Relationships with others is an area of weakness, and we struggle. We do relationships with a limp. No relationship can be taken for granted. They are too important, and we cherish every one.

If you are in the life of an autistic child, teen, or adult (no matter who you are, or the role you play), odds are good that you matter more to that person than you understand, and are making a difference that will last for the rest of their life. Thank you for the role you play. As a result of this kind of support, the eight year old boy mentioned in the opening is now older and is doing much better. He is being supported in many ways, including by peers. While relationships are still a struggle, he is no longer alone.

When talking about relationships, of all kinds, the issue of love comes up. Many are not too sure what to do with the idea of autism and love. With autism we can't think and feel at the same time, and don't do emotions well. I had a boss who once said I "don't ooze warm fuzzies." So how does someone autistic live a life with love? If love is defined right, very well.

What is love? Typically we think emotion. With autism we can and do feel the emotion of love. However, how we express that emotion may be different. It is most likely less "warm and fuzzy" and more "loyal problem solver".

Part of the problem of looking at love is that in English a lot of different meanings are combined within the single word, "love". Loving a spouse, loving a child, loving a friend, and loving a sibling all create very different images and ideas, but all use the word "love". Loving someone's country is different. Loving chocolate something different yet ... and how about loving the sweet taste of success? What is love? I use one definition for all love involving people. (Sorry chocolate ... it doesn't work for you.) It can apply to all relationships, regardless of age, gender, or romance. Due to a unique feature this definition works beautifully for those on the autism spectrum. It's not something I came up with, but is from a biblical passage commonly referred to as the love chapter:

> Love is patient, love is kind. It does not envy, it does not boast, it is not proud. It is not rude, it is not self-seeking, it is not easily angered, it keeps no record of wrongs. Love does not delight in evil but rejoices with the truth. It always protects, always trusts, always hopes, always perseveres. Love never fails. (I Corinthians 13:4–8a)

To me, this and nothing else is love. This definition provides a unique perspective of love for those who are on the autism spectrum. There is nothing in it about emotions or feelings. Absolutely nothing. It is all conscious decision and action. Warm fuzzies are irrelevant. Someone on the autism spectrum can meet this definition of love as easily as anyone.

Many have never been loved this way, or loved someone this way. Not just in a romantic relationship, but anyone ever. It looks pretty good. With autism we may be dressed a little funny, talk about odd things, say stupid stuff, and be complete cultural and social misfits. However, with this definition of love based on conscious decision and action, we can make absolutely amazing spouses, parents, friends, workers, and people to be around.

PART B

AUTISM CULTURE

10. AUTISM AS CULTURE

Culture is the common collection of customs, practices, values, goals, humor, history, art, and so on among a group of people. Often this is a large group, such as a nation. However, the larger the group the more subcultures will be contained within. For example, the rustic back mountains of Appalachia and the posh urban culture of Beverly Hills may both technically be "American culture" but the two are also very different. Hence the extreme contrast providing the premise of the 1960s television show *Beverly Hillbillies*.

With autism we have our own culture unique to being on the autism spectrum. The national or local culture we are living in may technically be our home culture, because we have lived our whole lives there, but due to autism it is not our true culture. The culture of autism is our real home culture. We are living, working, and trying to function in a culture that is not our own. I have worked with people on the spectrum from all over the world, and no matter what nation or culture someone grew up in, they all have the same base culture of autism that cuts across everything else.

An example of this would be that for a person on the autism spectrum truth and accuracy of information is more important than the emotions of a person. An autistic person would rather hurt someone else's feelings than tell an untruth, even if a polite "white lie". This is not desiring to cause someone harm, but is a differing order of priorities between autism and non-autism cultures.

I have lived most of my life in the Northeast United States. It is where I was born, raised, and spent almost all my adult life. People would call that my home culture. However, because I am on the autism spectrum I find I have more cultural aspects in common with those on the autism spectrum from all over the world than I do most of the people living in my neighborhood. That does not mean I dislike the non-autistic people around me. It only means we are from a different culture. It equally does not mean I like everyone on the autism spectrum. It only indicates that we share a common culture.

Once autism is identified and understood as a culture people tend to have an easier time understanding and working with those on the autism spectrum. It takes some of the mystery away. People know about cultures.

If someone is planning on traveling or hosting an international student they will study some of the culture to begin to become familiar with what they will encounter. Does this make them an expert in that culture? Of course not. But it is a starting place. From here, those not of the culture will begin to be aware of the differences so that when faced with the culture itself they can have greater success. Will they ever master the culture? Not unless a great deal of time is spent in full immersion (years). Even then, they will not understand and operate as seamlessly as a native who has lived their entire life in that culture would, but they can still become pretty good.

The same is true with autism and the autism culture. Those outside the autism culture can learn about it and have greater success. Those, such as parents and spouses, who have spent a great deal of time interacting with the autism culture can become pretty good if they work at it. However, even for them, after years, it is not their own culture and there needs to be a recognition that there will be some things that cannot be fully appreciated or understood.

Another factor at play is that just because someone has been exposed to a culture does not mean that they have begun to understand or appreciate that culture. We have all heard stories of the "ugly American" when it comes to international travel. They get stuck in a stage of culture shock and never get out of it. Nothing they encounter in the new culture is right or good. Only their culture from back home is. They make culturally inappropriate decisions, and they often become angry, agitated, and obnoxious. Not only is there lack of success in the culture, but significant regression in their adjustment.

This can happen in people's contact with the autism culture too. Rather than growing appreciation and understanding, and success through exposure, they get stuck. Autism and the autism culture is wrong. The only way things work is the way they know how, and the only path to success is the one they took in life. They often become angry, agitated, and obnoxious. Not only is there lack of success, but significant regression in their approach to autism.

The same is true for those who are autistic. They can learn to live in a culture not their own, the non-autistic culture. Since they have been doing it their whole life, over time they can become very fluent. However, as with anyone adjusting to any culture, it can be a lot of hard work, with the need to maintain elements of the autistic culture, especially in the privacy of their home. The autistic individual also benefits from someone who is aware of what is going on to help them learn to live in a culture not their own, which at times can be overwhelming and uncomfortable.

Just as with the concept of the "ugly American" refusing to give up their own cultural biases and practices when in another culture, it can happen with those on the autism spectrum too. They can get stuck along the process, and things fall apart, including their success. Anger, bitterness, unhappiness, lack of personal fulfillment, and/or a sense of superiority can all become problems. These are people who will refuse to adjust to the world, demanding the world adjust to them. It does not work.

While I support autism acceptance, we are in the minority and do not make the rules for the world. The world owes us nothing. It may not be fair, but it is reality. I, along with the rest of the world's population, need to live in reality, and not in the world as we would like it to be, or even as it should be.

Unfortunately there isn't the space in this book to completely detail autism culture. So I have tried to focus on the areas that are most important for understanding and for bridging the gap between the non-autism and autism cultures.

11. HOW THE BRAIN IS DIFFERENT

With autism emotions are instantly there, just like we flicked a light switch. The emotions can go away just as fast. This is universal with autism, regardless of the person's age or abilities. It is based in the brain itself. This feature of the autistic brain can be our best friend, or our worst enemy.

There are many who know neurology better than I do. I get disoriented reading neurology journals. It is like they have a secret language all their own. While I am going to talk about the brain, I will keep it simple and only focus on how it applies to everyday life on the autism spectrum.

Different parts of the brain specialize in different things. What we are going to focus on are the fact-based and emotion-based parts of the brain. If you want to show off to your friends and neighbors, the fact-based area is in the frontal lobe and the emotion-based area is in the temporal lobes. Just remember fact-based and emotion-based.

In a non-autistic person's brain the fact-based and the emotion-based areas talk to each other, and can work together. This allows a person to bring emotions into their facts. This is important for functions such as showing sympathy. It also allows them to regulate and rationalize their emotions. The world will not end because there is no more chocolate ice-cream.

In the autistic brain the fact-based and emotion-based parts of the brain do not communicate well with each other, or work well together. For our purposes they are essentially mutually exclusive, and only one or the other part of the brain will be dominant at any given time. While not technically correct, with autism, it could be said we cannot think and feel at the same time. That instant appearance and disappearance of emotions is the result of the dominant part of the brain switching from fact-based to emotion-based and back, just like flicking a light switch.

The first thing this means is that the autistic person can have a hard time appropriately expressing emotion. We can be called things like: cold, heartless, cruel, uncaring, and so on. I have seen a situation where an immediate family member was terminally ill, and close to death. The autistic person was asking about when the person would die, what will happen once they die, and so on. They were trying to process the facts of the situation, but from the view of cultural and emotional expectation, failing miserably in their role as a family member. The expected appearance of empathy was not there.

It is the brain being predominantly in fact-based mode that results in the stereotype of people on the autism spectrum being cold, aloof, uncaring, mean, robotic, or whatever other emotions which are not warm and fuzzy. They are functioning in fact mode in a situation where the non-autism world around them is functioning on an emotional level.

Probably more important for cultural functioning is that when an autistic person is feeling emotion, all fact-based rational thought is gone. Everything at this point is emotion driven. An overwhelming level of emotion is expected and accepted in Western culture at times of great tragedy. On September 11, 2001 the United States, and much of the world, was shocked and mourned deeply. But this extreme level of emotion is not expected or accepted when someone totally falls apart because the last chocolate chip cookie has been eaten. While such scenarios can be common with autism, they do not fit other cultural norms.

Typical non-autism-based methods of helping someone gain perspective and calm themselves not only do not work, but can make the situation worse with autism. We cannot rationalize and give perspective to a distraught person on the autism spectrum. The typical therapist maneuver of trying to talk someone down and work through the situation does not work. It is like throwing gasoline on a fire. The part of the brain that does the rational processing is not working right. This is why with autism, nothing can be dealt with in the moment, but needs to be deferred anywhere from hours, to days, if it can be discussed at all.

One of the other key ways that the brain is different with autism is that the amygdala, located in the temporal lobes, or emotion centers of the brain, is larger. The amygdala is the part of the brain in charge of sensory processing, and is the triggering mechanism for the fight / flight / freeze response. The sensory processing part of the brain being larger helps to explain some of the extreme sensory struggles people on the autism spectrum experience. And its relation to the fight / flight / freeze response can also help explain some of the intensity of emotion once a person on the autism spectrum is triggered.

12. HIGHS AND LOWS

Emotional ups and downs are a part of everyday life. With each high comes an equal and opposite low. This is not an autism thing. It happens to everyone. But what makes the experience unique with autism is that we are not wired to survive the extremes of these routine ups and downs.

As we discussed in the previous chapter, due to the communication problems between the fact and emotion centers of the brain, someone who is autistic could be said to not be able to think and feel at the same time. With the up and down cycles of life, there can be a lot of emotion-based thinking. At the low end we battle meltdowns, anxiety, and depression. On the high end, emotions are also felt strongly, with excitement, love, and euphoria.

While most of us want to feel more of those good emotions, they are still emotions. As such, when feeling them, the autistic person is not thinking well. Things can be said and done that cause problems. Bad decisions around alcohol, drugs, sex, fast driving, and so on can happen when feeling emotions on the high end. There may be regret later, but in the moment the part of the brain that can put the brakes on is not working.

With every high comes an equal and opposite low. We are in a cycle of ups and downs. This is unavoidable. Out of control good emotions are setting up for a crash. Every time I see an autistic kid so over the top excited they are totally "gone" there is a part of me that knows there will be a day of reckoning soon. The crash and low is coming, and not a thing can be done about it. It may be tonight. It may be tomorrow. But the low is coming.

When I first learned of this cycle as a teenager I set out to learn how to control it. I started trying to bring the down times up. No one wants to feel depressed, anxious, or otherwise miserable. It took me a couple of years to figure out there was very little that could be done on the low end of these emotional waves. While I now know some techniques, their effects are still limited. The trick of increased stability and success is, instead of trying to control the lows, we control the highs. Learning to control the highs will give control over the lows, lessening or eliminating the emotional crash and burn. With every high comes an equal and opposite low. The more we can control the up, the more we can control the down.

We take out the peaks and fill in the valleys. This gives us relative stability and the ability to function much more successfully in a world not set up for autism. More and more time is spent in the middle range where the fact-based part of the brain is in control.

I am often asked how to control the highs and lows. Honestly, it can take some time, and is a big-picture long-term process. It is worth the effort. I work with people on this process routinely.

The first step is to teach the person self-awareness, so they are able to identify where their line is for the brain to make the switch. While we focus on the high end for this technique, there are benefits to knowing the line on the low end too.

I taught myself where my line was by constantly analyzing my own clarity of thought, which is something I still do today. Typically the first sign that something is off is recognizing my thinking has become fuzzy. Fuzzy thinking can mean emotion.

While I have those I work with also monitor their clarity of thought, many times this level of self-awareness is very difficult for the person on the spectrum to achieve, especially in the beginning. So the way I often start to create awareness about where their emotional lines are is to teach them to monitor their own physiology. Things like: heart rate, muscle tension, where they are looking, body warmth, what their stomach feels like, or even speech rate.

Then when a person begins to approach the brain tripping into its emotional state, I teach them to disengage. Sometimes that may mean literally leaving the location they are in, even if for a few minutes, to de-escalate brain arousal. Disengagement can also be purely mental, where the person, through mental focus and discipline, disengages the brain enough to either de-escalate or plateau brain arousal before the line is crossed into emotional thinking. In both physical and mental disengagement the person can continue to have a good time, but remains in full control of themselves.

Sounds hard? It is, and remains one of the more difficult things for people to master. Even if it takes years to achieve this level of control (though it often does not) the success it can help bring in life is worth the time and effort. For those I work with we typically treat it as a long term goal, perpetually in the background, while also working on other easier to master success techniques.

13. MELTDOWN AND SHUTDOWN

When we think of someone on the autism spectrum being triggered we typically think of an explosive meltdown. It is one of the things that autism is well known for. However, while triggering with autism can result in a meltdown, it can also cause what is known as a shutdown.

Meltdown and shutdown both serve the same purpose. They are protective. Meltdown is exploding outward. Meltdown lets everyone know that there is a problem and the expectation is to fix it or get out of the way. Shutdown is collapsing inwards, building an invisible wall between the person and the problem. There is a neurological numbing or insulating effect towards the source of the problem. While those on the spectrum tend to be naturally wired more in favor of one way or the other, with autism we are naturally wired to do both. While outwardly they appear to be exact opposites, meltdown and shutdown both have the same triggering system in the brain, and serve the same protective role.

Meltdown

In the course of my work over the years I have dodged Legos, water bottles, iPads, and even feces. I have been kicked, hit, bitten and almost anything else that can be imagined. I even had a cute little six-year-old almost dislocate my jaw (head down ... ramming speed). Most people in and around the autism world know what a meltdown is.

Meltdowns are hard for everyone, especially the kid having the meltdown. Every now and then we need to be reminded of this. We know it is hard for us. We sometimes forget that the kid is having a worse time than we are. Despite the outward appearance, in a true meltdown they are not being oppositional and they certainly are not enjoying themselves. It is not about control or winning. It is about survival.

Meltdown is protective. It is driving everyone and everything away. It is loudly broadcasting to the world that they are in trouble, can't take it anymore, and someone needs to fix it. Every single person on the planet has a breaking point. Due to the difficulties of surviving in a world not set up for autism an autistic child typically reaches their breaking point before many others.

Be aware, a true meltdown is like a multi-directional flail. There is no pausing to see who is watching. There is no great coordination and precision, or seeking out something specific. I have gotten hit in the face as well as had my glasses thrown across the room, but that was purely because I was in the way. Other things got hit, and other things got thrown. If there seems to be too much control, focus, skill, or situational awareness on the part of the person, chances are good that we are not looking at an autism based meltdown. It is more likely a temper-tantrum or something mental health related. It is still emotion-driven, and with autism we cannot think and feel well at the same time, but it is likely not an autism driven meltdown.

Shutdown

Most people in and around the autism world have seen a shutdown. However, many probably missed it, or did not know what they were seeing. Shutdown is quiet, withdrawing from people and the world. It is an invisible psychological barrier between the person and the source of the problem that allows them to survive.

There can be multiple levels of shutdown, especially as the autistic person gains knowledge and experience. At one end is delayed response, being a little quiet, and slightly withdrawn. At the other end I have seen some kids go completely catatonic. They are totally non-responsive, limp, and will even have to be carried away from danger. Many levels lie between the mild and severe.

Shutdown is obviously preferable to meltdown. It scares fewer people, and as an adult allows someone to better maintain employment and functioning in society. But it is still very difficult for the autistic person. Just as with meltdown, they have reached their breaking point. The difference is that instead of an explosion, it is an implosion. All that negative energy and damage is turned inwards.

While preferable to meltdown, shutdown does have its problems. I have found it makes it harder to get an autistic child the help and services they need. When someone is getting screamed and sworn at, spit at, and possibly dodging a chair or two, it tends to be noticed and remembered. When a kid collapses in on themselves into a pile of goop it can be missed. They are too "good and quiet", sailing under the radar.

In Life

A shutdown should always be allowed and encouraged. While not perfect, it is the least bad option. If the shutdown option is taken away all that is left is meltdown.

For example, a child goes into shutdown. The teacher realizes the child isn't paying attention. The teacher attempts to break through the shutdown and redirect the student. If breakthrough is successful the protective defense of the shutdown is now gone. Meltdown is the only option left. There is an instant explosion, which in the incident report "came out of nowhere". (While this is a classroom example, there are many good teachers who do "get it", and this type of scenario can happen anywhere and with anyone.)

As this explosion was apparently unprovoked to the outside observer, the child now begins to develop a reputation of being oppositional, defiant, disrespectful, emotionally disturbed, or an otherwise problem kid.

I can and do teach autistic people to shutdown instead of meltdown. They need to be ready for this – often there needs to be other work done first – but when they are ready I have seen success very quickly. While not every person can be successful, with many on the autism spectrum meltdowns can be a thing of the past.

In the beginning we start by trying to avoid situations that would cause a meltdown. Eliminating all triggers and creating a managed environment may not represent reality, but the more success we can have in the beginning the better.

What we are going to do is teach the person to mentally block or "turn off" all sensory input, and focus on something else. They do this as soon as they begin to notice any frustration. With autism, we are naturally wired for shutdown just as much as meltdown, but sometimes it needs to be trained. It is the exact same triggering mechanism, only the focus of the energy is different.

We tell them at the beginning of frustration to turn off their ears, turn off their eyes, turn off their mouth, turn off their muscles, and not feel anything. Obviously they can still hear, see, etc. but we want the brain neurologically to ignore those signals. They are going into their own little world. Anything they are going to say or do needs to wait until the brain consciously tells them it is okay to do it or say it. We have them focus on something they like to think about and/or like to do.

In the beginning it will be a purely cognitive process. The more they go through this process the more it will become habit. Whenever possible, praise and/or reward the person for shutting down instead of melting down. This can be hard because someone can be so skilled at it that the shutdown may go unnoticed.

While working on this technique learning to shutdown rather than meltdown should be an ongoing project. It should be talked about at least every few days, and in the beginning especially we may want to talk about it several times a day, every day. Significant success can be often seen in days, and within a few months all meltdowns may be eliminated.

Once meltdowns are eliminated the next two goals are to shorten the length of time someone needs to be in shutdown, and reduce the depth of the shutdown. While a person on the autism spectrum will continue to go into some form of shutdown for the rest of their lives, the briefer and shallower the shutdowns are the more successfully they can function in society.

14. HARD-WIRED TRIGGERS

Based on individual life experience and how someone is wired each autistic person will have their own set of individual triggers. However, with autism there are four hardwired triggers common to all on the autism spectrum. Each one of these triggers results in either a shutdown or a meltdown. It is unavoidable. The triggers are hardwired. While a person who can manage the triggering process will be more successful than one who cannot, knowing what the triggers are so they can be avoided is even better.

Negative Emotion

The first of these four triggers is negative emotion, and may be the biggest and most problematic of the four.

If an autistic person is around someone who is agitated, frustrated, angry, or any other negative emotion they will mentally crash and fall apart. Meltdown or shutdown. It cannot be avoided.

This negative emotion does not need to be targeted at the autistic person. They just need to be around it and exposed. A professional gets frustrated with a student and the autistic kid at the other end of the room falls apart "for no reason". Two kids argue on the playground and the autistic kid who has nothing to do with either of them is a mess "for no reason". There is a reason. The reason is they are exposed to negative emotion.

This can happen at home. Parenting an autistic child can produce frustration. As a result there can sometimes be a bit of an "edge" to how a parent handles a situation (or they can explode all over the place and yell at the kid too). If there wasn't a meltdown or shutdown before, there will be one now. There must be total emotional calm and stability for someone on the spectrum to function.

I tell parents that unless someone is going to get hurt or the television is on its way out the window to walk away if they need to. This is not to say the situation isn't a problem and doesn't need to be dealt with. However, unless it can be handled with total calm it should not be handled at that moment. We need to be able to say "you can't pour paint on the dog" in the same tone of voice we tell them their chicken nuggets are ready.

Negative emotion is more than just yelling. It is the vocal tension of negative emotion that actually triggers. Loud may be a sensory problem, but it is not necessarily negative emotion. Think of those who are just loud and outgoing – they are not necessarily negative people. The negative emotion which triggers can be considered quiet, situationally appropriate and/or professional. It is the tension in the voice that does the triggering. And the result is meltdown or shutdown.

I have had some people tell me that negative emotion is a reality of life, and that autistic people need to learn how to deal with it. Sorry, but it cannot be done. I wish it could. This may be one of the few times

I view autism as a disability. There is no learning to live with negative emotion for those on the autism spectrum. Period.

Impressively, I see many people around those who are autistic work very hard to protect those on the spectrum from negative emotion. While at times it can be difficult, they understand its importance and that it is the right thing to do for the person on the autism spectrum.

For some people negative emotion is a way of life. I have cut all these people out of my life. They are not welcome. Yes, it is that simple. I am not punishing them or viewing them as bad people. I can't afford to continually be putting my life back together. It is hard enough already. I have no room in my life for people who are perpetually angry, negative, agitated people. All of them are gone. As a result I have a reasonably stable emotional environment. I rarely get triggered by negative emotion, because it isn't there to be triggered by. This allows me to function.

Negative emotion is probably the biggest consistent trigger for those on the autism spectrum. The child that is continually being triggered will not be able to succeed. The amount of trauma involved in constantly recovering from crashing, and never knowing when the next emotional upheaval will come, makes success difficult if not impossible.

One of the most important things that can be done for the success of an autistic individual is providing them a completely stable emotional environment. This may involve some work, some changes, and some hard decisions, but this stability is critically important to their success in life.

Surprise

The second of these four triggers is surprise. With autism we don't do surprise, and there is no such thing as good surprise. Good surprise is still better than bad surprise, maybe resulting in shutdown instead of meltdown, but it is still surprise.

With autism part of how we function and survive is to prepare ourselves intellectually for what is coming. If we rely on our instincts and natural responses we will have problems. As a result we work hard to anticipate what is coming and appropriately prepare.

If a little kid with autism is expecting to go to the bank, then the post office, and then the grocery store, and the order gets mixed up, or something is added, or a stop removed, they can be thrown. They will have been preparing themselves for what comes next, and when something else happens they are not ready. It can be a minor event. It can be a major event. Either way, they will be off.

There are techniques that as someone gets older can be learned to anticipate variables, the likelihood of those variables, and how to respond to each of those different variables, including the implications of each response. That is typically too much for a young child.

With a little kid as adults we need to do some of that processing for them. We communicate our plans to them, but as we do that, we also communicate other things that may happen, both that are within our control and out of our control. The likelihood of these variables can also be communicated. As we change our minds, or other information enters the equation that can impact outcomes, we share this as well.

While giving all information and variables can create stress, it is beginning to help them process and understand how to predict and cope with what is coming. "I am planning on stopping at the game store. I think it is open until 8pm, but it might close earlier today because it is Sunday. If it is closed we will instead go home and come back tomorrow after school."

Such a narrative does a few things. 1) Gives intent of what is next. 2) If the plan does not happen, it explains why it does not happen. 3) Then, an explanation of what to anticipate if the plan changes, and the solution for when they can get to the game store. With this, they may be slightly stressed. "Oh no, what if it is closed." But they will also know that if closed it is not the end of the world, and while upset, there are solutions.

This open communication also builds trust that we will be open and honest with them, and share information as we know it. Again, they may not be happy, but it is less likely to be at us. We reduce the likelihood of: "You said we could go to the game store, and now we can't. You lied!" We tell them what we know, when we know it, as well as how we know it. It is beginning to help them process on their own.

Surprise is no better as an autistic adult. The level of surprise in the example given is often not a big deal. However, significant and intentional surprise can be. I remember being told by a friend that they would pick me up at a certain time, and we would do something, but refused to give any details. I hated it. I had no idea how to prepare myself mentally. I also had no idea: how to dress, if I should eat first, when I would be home, what I should bring, and so on. I hated every element of the experience, including before, during, and after.

What many do not understand is that disappointment falls into the same category as surprise. It is as if the whole world is going to end when an autistic child encounters a minor disappointment that many adults think they should have been able to anticipate, or even if they could not anticipate it, that the child's response is completely out of proportion to the disappointment.

For example, an autistic child plays a carnival game. In their mind they have already won. There is no other possibility. How could there be? They have won, the stuffed animal is theirs, and actually playing the game is little more than a formality. When this does not happen there is surprise. With surprise, the child is triggered. While it may outwardly appear like the child is a spoiled immature brat, with autism they typically are not. It is the surprise factor.

We as adults know this should not surprise them, but it does. They do not have the same perspective of the world, nor the capabilities yet to run realistic probabilities. As before when shopping, we can prep them ahead of time so they are ready for the various outcomes. They may be disappointed, and may not like what is being said, but it can reduce the surprise factor and help with overall life perspective.

I know my parents prepared me, telling me the odds, and also refusing to let me play the carnival games. I of course was frustrated, and many times told them they didn't know what they were talking about. At ten I went to a carnival with a friend and his family. At the rate of a quarter a game I quickly blew through the five dollars I brought with me. I was not happy, but due to being adequately prepared the surprise was mild. I processed the odds, realized my parents were correct, and have never played a carnival game again. Maybe one of the most important five dollars I have spent in my life.

Disappointment being surprise in a carnival game is easy to illustrate. However, surprise being a trigger is true in all areas of life. That is why educating someone about probabilities is so critical. Without understanding probabilities an autistic person will stress and panic needlessly over extremely rare things that likely will never happen, as well as be surprised by highly probable outcomes. Neither is good.

I do see a certain percentage of kids I work with who are amazingly flexible with daily routine. Talking with these families, what they all have in common is that their child never knew routine. Everything in their home is unpredictable random chaos. As they never knew anything different, the state of not knowing was typical for them, and therefore not a surprise.

Every kid is different and every home is different. I have learned through anticipatory analysis how to minimize surprise, and am only surprised a few times a year. However, when it does occur I am just as overwhelmed and lost as a little kid. The issue that triggers meltdown or shutdown is the actual surprise itself. Whether a common occurrence or rare, with autism surprise ends badly.

Sensory Overload

The third of these hardwired triggers is sensory overload.

Sensory overload is when something is too itchy, loud, bright, smelly, the wrong sound frequency, or any other sensory stimuli that pushes a person to their breaking point. A person may seek sensory stimulation in some ways, but they will be overwhelmed and avoid it in others. When they can't take it anymore they will be triggered into a shutdown or meltdown, just as with the other hardwired triggers.

The stimuli that cause the overload may be using the same sense that a person is using for sensory seeking in some other way. For example, I am easily overloaded by artificial scents that are designed to be pleasant (candles, soaps, deodorants, potpourri, perfumes, air fresheners, and so on) but I love the smell of skunk. Yes, the smell of the animal skunk.

What any one autistic person is able to tolerate can and will be different than any other autistic person. While I need to avoid artificial scents, I work with some kids who will seek them out. Everything comes down to an individual mix that varies from person to person.

Sometimes just having control over the stimuli is what makes the difference. An autistic person may like their music loud. It is sensory seeking for them. Yet that same person might be totally unable to stand listening to the neighbor's music at any volume. The issue is not failing to understand the other person's perspective or dislike of the music. The music is legitimately triggering them in a sensory way purely because there is an inability to escape.

Sensitivity to sensory stimuli can change. Anxiety levels are an example of a common factor that influence autistic people's sensory sensitivity. The higher the anxiety the more sensitive they are to negative sensory stimuli. This can create a self-feeding cycle where the anxiety creates greater sensitivity, and then the irritation from the greater sensitivity increases the anxiety, and so on. This self-feeding cycle can quickly spiral out of control as that person reaches the point where the sensory input is overwhelming and they are triggered into meltdown or shutdown.

It is often necessary for an autistic person to do things to control or change their sensory environment to survive. The techniques are flee, block, or avoid.

1) Flee.

There are times an autistic person needs to flee what is causing the problem before they fall apart. I have been chased out of stores by crying babies, people cutting ceramic tile, subwoofers, different scents, and other irritants. I have also changed clothes because of annoyances like tags or seams, turned off lights because of being triggered by the specific light frequency, and even had to walk out of restaurants because of the chaotic sounds.

Sometimes it is too much, and fleeing the sensory problem is the only solution. One word to those reading this who are not autistic. If you are fortunate enough to have the autistic person tell you: "I need to get out, and I need to get out now", they really do mean right now. "We will go in a minute" or "It isn't that bad" are not answers that will work. The hardwired trigger of sensory overload will trip, resulting in a meltdown or a shutdown.

2) Block.

There are times the autistic person will be able to block the sensory irritant, and be able to continue what they were doing. The most common example of this is the use of headphones when sounds are a problem. One word of caution is if they are used all the time, the brain begins to compensate, and already sensitive hearing becomes even more sensitive. One of my favorite sensory blocking tools is a white noise sound screen called "Dohm", from Marpac, available online. With scent I have even been known to wear a respirator to block some smells.

3) Avoid.

Sometimes the only solution is to know which particular sensory triggers affect us and avoid going to places where we know they will be. There are stores I can't get anywhere near based on smell alone. At times I can't identify the specific trigger but I know to avoid it anyway. For example, I know I am triggered by something in the new section of Destiny Mall here in Syracuse. Even on a good day the longest I have spent there is about ten minutes. I don't know why. The light frequency, some type of vibration, a sound, something about the colors? I don't know, but I have learned I need to stay away.

Please realize that those of us on the autism spectrum are significantly more sensitive to sensory stimuli. It is not something made up. While we can often manage it, when we reach a certain threshold we are triggered into meltdown or shutdown. As much as we don't like it, there is no alternative.

Pecked to Death by Ducks

The fourth of these triggers is being pecked to death by ducks. This is the same as "The straw that broke the camel's back", but less of a cliché.

The problem itself that causes the triggering isn't always the actual problem. We may have dealt with the same situation just fine yesterday, and will deal with it just fine tomorrow. However, right now we can't, and we fall apart. The real issue here is the cumulative buildup of minor problems over time. We have been exposed to a series of irritants and stressors and have finally reached a breaking point.

Perhaps we didn't sleep well. The alarm is obnoxious, our favorite shirt is dirty, the cereal got soggy, it is too hot out, the bus smells funny, and so on. By the time we get to "being out of our favorite snack" we can't take it. We are triggered and fall apart.

People are often surprised by this one, because they can't figure out why it is as if the whole world is going to end over a seemingly minor issue that has been dealt with successfully many times before. Every person on this planet has a breaking point. With autism it is a lower threshold, with many more issues in the day cumulatively building toward that final peck of the duck, and we are done. The final duck pecks. Meltdown or shutdown.

15. BRAIN SWITCH

When an autistic person is thinking emotionally every action and decision is based on emotion. Rational thought and logic are gone. If it is negative emotion they are triggered. Everything is then driven by how they make the problem go away. This can mean meltdown. While emotional highs can cause difficulties, as we've already seen, it is the state of negative emotion and meltdowns most of us want to fix.

Once triggered, how do we get the brain to switch from emotion-based thinking back to fact-based thinking? The way most people are taught to deal with crisis, such as talking through the situation and offering solutions, does not work with autism. It can make the problem worse.

If I am in meltdown because we are out of chocolate ice-cream, telling me that we have vanilla, or saying we can get more chocolate tomorrow, will not work. All that is accomplishing is reminding me that I do not have my chocolate ice-cream. The meltdown continues.

What needs to be focused on is how to get the brain to make the switch from emotion-based thinking to fact-based thinking. Focus on the brain, not the problem at hand. There are three ways to get the brain to switch from emotion back to fact, ending the crisis.

Time

This method is inconvenient because it requires time we typically do not have, but it does work, and I do use it. If we wait the person out, without anything new to trigger them, the autistic brain all on its own will make the switch from emotion-based thinking back to fact-based thinking.

When I say nothing new to trigger them, this can be as sensitive as body language, talking, eye contact, or other subtle factors. To do this, don't speak and avoid eye contact. Look down and to the side, using peripheral vision. I think of this approach as calm persistence. We are not giving up and going away, but we are also not contributing to the problem. We are waiting it out.

How long will this take? It is different with everyone. Maybe ten minutes. Maybe twenty. Maybe an hour. We can't be sure, but with experience we will know when it is over. There is a shift in body language and facial expression. It is as if the person becomes more aware and connected with their surroundings. But if in doubt, wait longer. Most people do not wait long enough. If the wait has not been long enough the autistic person will retrigger and the clock will start over. Often what could have been a relatively short unpleasant time gets extended by multiple retriggers. Instead of a single shorter meltdown, these shorter times get strung together by retriggering into what can end up being a several-hour event. If waited out properly the first time, the event will be over much more quickly.

Special Interest

It is nearly impossible for an autistic person to be upset, angry, or agitated, when actively engaged in their special interest (special interests are covered extensively in the next chapter).

However, we cannot just give someone their special interest when they go into meltdown. We are then rewarding inappropriate behavior. It will not take our kids long to learn that all they need to do to get what they want is behave badly.

One way to use special interest properly is preventatively. If we notice tension building we can encourage them to access their special interest. Nothing bad has happened so we are not rewarding inappropriate behavior. This can restore the reserves and stabilize them. The meltdown is avoided.

The other way to use special interest preventatively is when we know we are entering a trigger-rich environment. For example, if grocery shopping is a historical problem, we can improve the outcome by providing the special interest before going in, and using the special interest all the time while shopping.

We have all experienced the moment when we say to ourselves "I should have given them the 'X' five minutes ago". At this point they are in meltdown and we do not want to reward inappropriate behavior. Special interest can still be used. We get them to associate getting the special interest with doing the right thing. In this meltdown let them know as soon as they behave appropriately – and that means stop yelling, kicking, throwing, biting, or whatever specific list needs to be given – we can then give them their special interest. "Be good" or "Behave appropriately" are meaningless, vague phrases. We need to be specific when stating what we expect for them to get what they want or need.

Within ten to twenty seconds of getting the good behavior, provide the special interest. We can't wait much longer than that. That would be viewed as a deal breaker. "I did what you asked and I did not get my batman figure. You lied!" It might seem that waiting such a short period of time would be seen as rewarding the inappropriate behavior. However, it is not. Within the brain the association is with the good behavior which we want to reinforce and encourage.

Cognitive Engagement

This tool is my favorite. As we've explored, with autism it is almost impossible to think and feel at the same time. Cognitive engagement is based on the idea that if we can get the autistic person thinking, engaging the fact-based parts of the brain, we are instantly turning off the emotionally driven meltdown at the biological level. To someone who is not autistic this technique may appear like distraction, but it is not. It is biologically forcing the brain to switch in the way we want.

What is being thought about must have no negative emotion tied to it. What I will typically do with an older child or adult is say: "We are going to go through the alphabet, and with each letter I want you to give me an animal that begins with that letter. What is an animal that begins with 'A'?" By the time we reach letters "G" or "H" the brain has usually made the switch back to being fact-based. Of course, being rule-oriented we need to finish the alphabet. (Remember "x-ray fish", and I have been known to stoop to using "unicorn".)

If possible I will combine special interest with cognitive engagement. If a child has a special interest in Pokémon, we will go A to Z with Pokémon instead of animals. If the special interest is trains we will go A to Z with things having to do with trains. We don't need to know the answers. They will.

Going A to Z is just one example of questions that I like to use. It can be anything. "What are the colors of the rainbow?" While that may be too easy for me, it may not be for someone else. If someone gets stuck we will help, often giving them an answer, and/or encourage them to move on. We don't want triggering due to frustration. The main point is we want to biologically force the fact-based part of the brain to work.

It does not matter if the autistic person knows what we are doing with the cognitive engagement technique. It works because it is biologically driven. To answer fact-based questions we need to access the fact portion of the brain, and in doing so we shut down the emotion portion of the brain. There is no other option. Ideally someone can learn to do this cognitive engagement technique on themselves. I use this technique on myself successfully. I created the technique and know everything about it, and it still works.

It does not matter if the person cooperates. I have one kid I work with who feels he deserves his meltdown. Because of this he will give a wrong answer every time. The beautiful thing is for him to know he is giving a wrong answer he must first figure out what the correct answer is. To do that he must access the fact-based portion of his brain. This shuts off the emotion centers of the brain, and the meltdown ends.

Remember, we do not want to retrigger them through frustration. There are times someone is too far gone, or is younger, and this level of cognitive engagement is too hard for them to do. In this case we back it off one cognitive step. We ask "observe and report" type questions. "How many fingers do I have up?" "What color is this?" "Is that door open or closed?" These may be enough by themselves, or they can be used to prime the pump, allowing us to move on to the more difficult type questions first mentioned.

For those who want to do the technique as perfectly as possible, when asking the questions it is best to: slow your rate of speech, lower the volume, soften the tone of voice, flatten the range to as close to monotone as possible, at the end of the question pitch the tone down instead of up (up can signal challenge, whereas down signals honesty), and avoid eye contact. Look down and to the side, using peripheral vision. I find this cognitive engagement technique also works with sign language or other forms of communication.

16. SPECIAL INTEREST

A proper understanding of special interest is critical for success with autism. If understood and harnessed special interests can be a powerful tool. If misunderstood and not handled properly they can destroy an autistic person.

Identifying the Interest

In my work with autistic children and adults I always ask if there is a special interest, and what it is. Nearly universally I get a smile and nod, followed by often entertaining stories of the special interest. Families seem relieved to be able to tell these stories to someone who understands and can appreciate the role the interest plays.

What is a special interest? A special interest is whatever the autistic person is obsessed over. It is whatever must be collected, talked about, played with, studied, and/or seemingly takes over their life. It can fall into a few categories.

First, it can be something very unique.

I worked with a six-year-old who collected hair driers. Every time a hair dryer entered the house he would take it. Mom would try to sneak one into the house – just like one he already had– to be able to dry her hair, but never got away with it. Each one would be confiscated and added to his collection. One might be good, but two was better. She finally gave up. Each day she would go to him and sign out a hair dryer from his collection, the same way someone would sign out a library book. When done with the hair dryer she would check it back into his collection. We were glad he had a lending program.

I worked with a family whose teen was into toilet plumbing parts. If you want to know how much duct tape it takes to keep the toilets in a house from being taken apart, I know people who can tell you.

Another client when he was very young had a special interest in vacuum cleaners. He had a toy vacuum cleaner that he would play with for hours daily. He would often just sit in the closet with it. It even got tucked in with him at bedtime every night.

Kids can have a special interest in things such as meteorology, geography, codes, antiques, or the dates famous people died. An eight-year-old I know does high-end math in his head for fun. I know another young child who has a special interest in cleaning. Some of these interests may not seem out of place for an adult, but are notable when seen in a child.

Second, a special interest can be something thought of as age appropriate and "typical", but the level of intensity and involvement with the interest is significant.

Very common examples of this are things such as: Thomas the Tank Engine, Pokémon, stuffed animals, Star Wars, Harry Potter, super heroes, Legos, or video games. Unfortunately, some dismiss this kind of special interest, seeing it as "typical". But due to the intensity and extent of the interest there is nothing "typical" about it.

Someone I knew had as his primary special interest Scooby-Doo. He knew the writers and directors for every episode and film He had multiple Scooby toys, books, and games, which no one was allowed to touch. Not me, not his mother, not anyone. He would show us, but he would always hold them. He would borrow Scooby books from the library that he already owned. We were also subjected to pop-quizzes of Scooby trivia. I still think I should have gotten credit for my answer of "bugs" when asked what is on the front of the Mystery Machine.

An instance as significant as the previous example most people would catch, but special interests are not always so easy to identify. A child may love watching Pokémon. They have the stuffed animals. They collect hundreds and even thousands of the cards. They play Pokémon on their game system. Is it a special interest? There are indicators to look for. It has to do with the role the special interest plays in emotional stability, and in the relative priority it has to everything else. Special interest is always number one.

Thirdly, a special interest can be a person, or involve a person.

While generally this type of special interest is seen more with teens or adults, I see this in children too. I have occasionally been the subject of the special interest. These kids rather insistently want to come live with me, and if they can't do that they want to at least spend time with me every day. I have also had times in my life when I have had other people as my special interest. Almost every autistic adult I have talked to has at some time in their life had another person as their special interest.

As long as it can be controlled, and is reciprocal, there can be isolated benefits to another person being a special interest. Unfortunately it rarely happens that way, and instead involves lots of frustration and heartache. If another person is the subject of a special interest, it can often be overwhelming for that person, destroying a friendship.

This is the common path these relationships follow, and autistic adults usually have a wealth of stories like this that end in frustration, hurt, and regret. This is likely a part of why having people as a special interest isn't often talked about. It can be an embarrassing and/or painful topic.

Combine poor interpersonal skills with the powerful drive and need of a special interest and it can be difficult to balance, and end in disaster. Even though the autistic person intellectually knows the subject of their special interest has obligations, families, work/school, and other interests, the drive surrounding an autistic special interest can be so strong they are often unable to control their impulse and need for access to the person.

So what is and what is not a special interest? What the special interest actually is can be literally anything. At what point do we cross that line from a hobby or even friendship to a special interest? I separate out special interest by the emotional and psychological role that interest plays in the person's life, and the intensity of that role.

Understanding Special Interests

This section will deal with frequently asked questions about autistic special interests.

1) Does everyone on the autism spectrum have a special interest?

It appears to be nearly universal, but it is not a diagnostic requirement to have a special interest. I occasionally have a client where we are unable to identify a clear special interest. I suspect that the handful who do not outwardly appear to have a special interest actually do have one.

This idea was supported a few months ago with a thirteen-year-old boy I work with. I was discussing special interests with him, and their importance in an autistic life, and role as a powerful tool. We were struggling to identify his special interest. After several minutes the thirteen-year-old admitted that he has a special interest, but that it was personal and private, and that he was not willing to discuss it with anyone.

I reassure people that keeping things private is their right, and neither I nor anyone else needs to know what it is, as long as they do. I can teach about special interests, and how to use special interests, without knowing what the interest is. In this case it was clearly an interest that broke the "typical" special interest mold. He later revealed his interest, and it was nothing bad, but something he found embarrassing.

Unique and hard to identify interests I have seen include: schooling, a spouse and the marital relationship, helping the community, being a girly girl, a handful of specific musical pieces, learning to understand people, movie production, faith and Christianity, someone's career, making pickles, a specific holiday, sports (often missed as being typical), and fishing (also missed as being typical). I could list many more. One parent told me that her son's special interest was spools of thread in teacups. A special interest really can be anything.

Though unpleasant to consider, it is also possible that a special interest may include something illegal, immoral, or otherwise seriously problematic or dangerous. I have encountered this professionally, and these people are not interested in broadcasting their special interest to the world. However, it is still a special interest.

2) How does someone get a special interest?

Where a special interest comes from is a mystery to many, including those on the spectrum themselves. It cannot be picked for another person. I know parents who have tried to pick an interest for their child, and had it end in total failure. Even the autistic person is unable to intellectually pick their own special interest. From their perspective it just sort of happens.

The creation of a special interest appears to happen with a spark at the joining of both experience and good emotion. Through experience a person realizes that something fascinates them, is something they are good at, or some other emotionally charged triggering mechanism takes place.

While a parent or others cannot pick a specific special interest for their child, they can create a fertile field of good things for their child to have both an experiential and emotional connection to. As some type of experience is an element in special interest selection, naturally exposing your kids to things as a part of life that would make good special interests improves the odds.

On the flipside, if you are horrified that your child's special interest may be zombies, swimsuit models, or an annoying kids' show, remember if they have no exposure to or experience with it then it is almost impossible for it to become a special interest. We cannot pick the interest, but we can pick the environment the special interest will take spark in.

3) Do special interests change with time?

Yes, special interests can and typically do change with time. The timetable for when the special interest changes is different with every person and every special interest. I have seen special interests last only a few weeks, and some last as long as decades.

Just as with selection, the change of a special interest is also driven by an experiential and emotional process. Just because an autistic person intellectually desires a different special interest does not mean it can or will happen. From the perspective of the autistic individual the change just sort of happens. They can be as surprised as everyone else.

Trying to externally get someone to change their special interest is very dangerous. It is perceived as a threat to the special interest. As a professional I will only consider undertaking helping someone to change a special interest if the interest is illegal, immoral, or somehow dangerous, and the person themselves intellectually wants the special interest to change. It is still a long process and high risk undertaking. How high risk? I'm not prepared to put the methodology or technique in print. It is that high risk.

4) Is it possible to have multiple special interests?

Yes, there can be more than one special interest: there is one primary at any given time, but this can change even throughout the day. I know someone that has had a specific primary special interest for most of his life. He is adamant about what his special interest is. There will be a crying fit if there is any hint from anyone that he might have a secondary interest, in addition to his primary special interest. Yet, even this person has other secondary special interests. We just don't point it out to him.

One interest is primary at any given moment in life, but having multiple secondary and even tertiary interests is quite common. Not always, but typically a secondary or tertiary special interest is a special interest that was a former primary special interest, now replaced by a new primary interest. It still holds some power, but nothing compared to the power of the current primary interest at the time.

5) What are my special interests?

As I write this I have two special interests which are very close in priority, and I can go back and forth between them even within a day, allowing myself a higher level of success and stability. The first special interest is autism. I love autism, autistic kids, teens, adults, and everything associated with it. This interest has served me well in my career working in the field of autism. I truly love what I do. My other special interest is Eighteenth Century artisan work. Most commonly I make and engrave powder horns, and build flintlock muskets and rifles, as well as many other accoutrements.

Special interests I have had over the years include: canning food, maps and map reading, squirrels, coin collecting, stuffed animals, art, photography, and many more. Some such as photography are more recent, and others such as stuffed animals, squirrels, and art have not been a primary special interest for me for decades. Some remain secondary or tertiary special interests. They do not hold the same power as the primary special interest, but there is still a little something there that can help to provide support if the benefit of the primary special interest is needed but unable to be accessed.

The earliest special interest I am aware of having was hats. This hat special interest took hold even before my first birthday. (Hats currently do not make the special interest list at any level.)

Importance of Special Interest

It is essential to understand how important the special interest is to an autistic person. It is the most important thing in their life. An autistic person will give up anything to be able to access their special interest. This includes: sleep, food, health, safety, money, work/school, and even people.

The special interest also plays a critical role in the autistic person's stability. If an autistic person is unable to access their special interest for a period of time they will start to emotionally fall apart. They can begin to be unable to: sleep properly, eat right, mentally focus, and may become physically ill. They can also become agitated and/or depressed. They will start to fall apart on multiple levels. I have even seen it result in hospitalization.

Because of its role in stability with autism, special interest is a need, and should be treated as a need. The level of that need is hard to communicate to non-autistic people. To help understand, think of it as food. Instead of thinking "Pokémon", "Thomas the Tank Engine", "meteorology" or whatever the special interest is, insert the word "food" in its place. Only then will someone begin to understand the role it plays.

Because special interest is a real need it should not be taken away. I know some, including professionals, will say find out what matters most to a child and use that as leverage to influence their behavior. Do not do this with an autistic special interest. It can destroy them and your relationship with them.

Denial of needs such as food, water, or sleep, might influence behavior, yet none of us would do it. It is abusive, and the idea horrifies us. We would understand that the damage being done to the child outweighs the changed behavior. The same is true for autistic special interest. Removal of the special interest to change a child's behavior may work in the short term, but the overall damage that is being done far outweighs any benefit. This damage and instability will put the child in a much worse place than before.

Loss of a special interest is one of the most devastating and dangerous things that can happen to an autistic person. The extent of the trauma and lifelong impact cannot be understated. It can result in psychiatric hospitalization, or worse. Loss of a special interest is an emergency, and should be treated as such. No matter the ultimate outcome, this is a life-changing experience.

If there is a loss or temporary loss of the primary special interest, a secondary special interest can be used to help support the person. This use of the secondary special interest in place of the primary interest can help keep the person from a total crash, but it cannot replace the restorative balance that is provided by the primary special interest. It is a temporary and inadequate support, but is better than nothing.

A much more common event than loss of the special interest is something seen as threatening the special interest. Whether that threat is real or only perceived does not matter. There will be a very strong reaction from the person. I cannot overstate how strong the reaction may be. It often catches people by surprise.

For example, say we have a child whose special interest is Thomas the Tank Engine. Another child who is over to play wants to play with the Thomas the Tank Engine. We are desperate for our child to make a friend. It is an interest they can connect over. We let the other child play with one of our child's Thomas toys. All of a sudden our autistic child is screaming bloody murder as they beat the other kid over the head. We messed with the special interest in a way that was seen as a threat.

Or say our child's special interest is aircraft. On the way home we are going to stop near the airport so they can watch the planes take off and land. Things are going great, but after a while it is time to go. We gave all the countdown warnings, and ultimately start to pull away. Our child starts begging to stay longer. We say if this is what will happen when we come to the airport we will stop coming for a while. At this point absolute panic hits and they are totally out of control. We messed with the special interest in a way that was seen as a threat.

Or perhaps our child's special interest is stuffed animals. There are hundreds around the house and we just can't take it anymore. Several end up in a box to be given away or sold. Our child discovers this and is as upset as you have ever seen them about anything. We understood they would be unhappy, but in our mind they are acting totally irrationally and out of proportion. We messed with the special interest in a way that was seen as a threat.

These are just three scenarios. All of them actually happened. The common thread is that anything seen as a threat to the special interest will result in a strong negative reaction. This is because of how important that special interest is to them and the role it plays with their stability. What is perceived as a threat may vary from child to child, but once a threat is perceived a strong over-the-top emotional reaction will result. This too can result in trauma and damage over time.

I understand that from a non-autistic perspective life cannot be all about special interest. There are obligations that need to be taken care of. Things such as productivity, life balance, and delayed gratification are necessary for success, but just because something is important or necessary does not mean that it is possible. The special interest comes first.

It may seem like we are painting a negative picture of an autistic person's experience with special interest. There can be challenges. It is an area of vulnerability. However, because special interest plays such a powerful role, it can also be a powerful tool. Special interest can be used to help stabilize, connect with others, create employment, and all around help the autistic person be successful in life in ways well beyond what was thought possible.

Special Interest as a Tool

There are many ways that understanding autistic special interest can be used as a tool to help the autistic person be more successful in life. I have selected four significant ways, but don't be limited by this list.

1) Stability.

One of the most powerful ways special interest can be used is to support stability. It is almost impossible for an autistic person to be upset or agitated when actively engaged with their special interest.

I'll share a personal example of how special interest can provide stability. I dislike flying, and hate turbulence. I have written sections of this book while at thirty thousand feet in an airplane during significant turbulence. It has been bad enough I had trouble hanging onto the computer. However, I was focused on and involved in my special interest of autism. As a result, I was successful in managing my anxiety from the turbulence.

I encourage others to use special interest in a similarly preventative way. When approaching an activity that is difficult for someone on the autism spectrum, provide the special interest before and during the activity. This may help them endure what might otherwise trigger them and cause them to fall apart.

Many autistic kids have difficulty with grocery shopping. From a sensory management perspective it is just too overwhelming. For a kid like this, provide the special interest in the parking lot, or while on the way. Then have them continue to engage with the special interest throughout the shopping experience. It may not be perfect, as there are no sure things in life, but it will almost certainly be better than it otherwise would have been.

2) Emotional reserves.

Emotional reserves are like a cup of pennies. Everything in life, even good things, cost some pennies. Sometimes a lot. Sometimes a little. The goal is to make it through the day without running out of pennies. Running out of pennies is bad. Very bad.

Much of life with autism is focused on not spending pennies we do not need to spend, so we may have a few left at the end of the day. Resources management. However, there is one way, and only one way, to put pennies back into the cup throughout the day. That one way is special interest. Through involvement with our special interest we can replenish spent emotional reserves, and be significantly more likely to make it through the day successfully.

I was called in to observe a school situation where the autistic child was an emotional mess and falling apart badly enough that he was becoming aggressive and hurting people. The school was trying to use the special interest as a reward. He did his work and then he could have the special interest.

As I was watching the tension build within this child I told the person working with him to give him his special interest, a toy car. They refused to do so because he had not finished all his work, therefore had not earned it. I told them again to give him the item. They again refused. The claim was that all he would do is play with the item and nothing would be done for the rest of the day unless they took it away from him. After several of these exchanges, and refusals by school staff, I pulled out a toy car that I brought with me, and gave it to him.

The child played with what I had given him for ten to fifteen seconds (while I was being glared at by several school district adults). He then put it next to himself as he sat down and completed all his work. He kept the special interest item I gave him, and had a great rest of the day. The kid did not have the strength and stability to be able to do what was being asked of him. By providing the special interest, it restored the strength and stability he needed.

I have many kids who carry with them to school their autistic special interest, or have it provided for them once they get there. They have that item or have access to it every minute. It is an important part of what allows them to survive a day.

3) Connect with others.

Special interest can also be used to assist with connecting with others. With autism there are struggles with interpersonal connectedness, social awareness, and the ability to make and/or maintain relationships with others. By bonding over a common interest, that interest can function to support a relationship where otherwise there might be none. It also increases contact with people, giving real-life opportunity to practice interpersonal skill development.

4) Employment.

Often with autism we focus on the deficits and what cannot be done. They are real, and there is some reason for that focus. However, there are also strengths that come with autism, and a special interest can be one of those strengths.

An autistic person is functioning at their absolute best when involved in their special interest. It is something they enjoy doing, and is something they must do to function properly and remain balanced. Due to the drive involved, and the obsessive intensity, a great deal of expertize is often developed in the area of the special interest. There is the potential to literally be the best in the world at what they do. The rest of their life may be a mess, but the individual can remain stable and excel in the area of their special interest.

The incredible skill that can come from employment in a person's area of special interest can make them excellent at what they do, making it easier for employers or customers to overlook the social, interpersonal, and cultural awkwardness that is a part of life for those of us on the spectrum. If a plumber is brilliant there is little concern that they are a bit odd. The pipes are fixed and that is what matters.

I am an example of being able to use special interest for employment. My special interest is autism, which has helped me be very good at what I do. And not only do I love my work, but I actually use this connection with autism as a part of my stability. I am at my best and happiest when working. Another well-known example would be Temple Grandin.

Her work within the cattle industry is as a result of her special interest. There are many others, mostly less well-known, who through their special interest are able to support themselves. I see them everywhere. I have encountered: college professors, engineers, medical personnel, mechanics, and many more. These individuals work not because they have to, for the money, or out of fear; they love what they do, and do it because it is a part of them.

17. SENSORY

There are significant sensory issues that accompany autism. There is sensory avoidance, where the sensory input is too much and overwhelming, causing the person to trigger and/or flee. There are also sensory seeking issues, where a person needs a type of input for improved stability and functioning. Common examples of this could be deep pressure or a fidget, but the range of inputs is significant. The needs will vary from person to person, and moment to moment.

Most can't understand what it is like to live with autism's sensory issues. What is it like? It is like needing to go to the bathroom, but you can't. It begins to take over every area of your life until that need is met.

Sensory needs impact the ability to focus and function. While it may start out feeling uncomfortable, it can gradually reach a point where the need becomes painful. If someone really needs to go to the bathroom they will not be able to work, listen, eat, sleep, or do anything that is a regular part of their day. They gotta pee. Nothing else matters. Life stops until this need is met. It is the same with autism-based sensory needs.

What happens when our autistic kids have an unmet sensory need, and they have to get something else done? All they can think about is that need to spin, bounce, rock, swing, fidget, or whatever else the need is. School work, chores, friends, what we are trying to tell them and everything else in the world no longer matters. They must get that sensory need met.

Who would tell a child that it is not yet time to go to the bathroom? Who would make a child earn the privilege of peeing? I would hope no one. Yet, these approaches are used with sensory needs. "It is not time for your sensory break." "We can't do sensory because occupational therapy is tomorrow after lunch." "Before you can have a sensory break you need to finish your work." When sensory input is needed, it is needed. With autism, managing sensory needs is a way of life.

Let's look at going to the bathroom as a service that is provided, such as meeting sensory needs are often discussed in a school setting. Is it meeting an academic need? Is it a required part of the day? "I'm sorry but going to the bathroom takes away from valuable classroom time, and we are only responsible for meeting the academic needs of your child."

Clearly this would or should never be said. The freedom to be able to use the bathroom is an understood need that everyone shares. The need for managing different types of sensory input is a physical need only some of us share. As a result, not everyone understands the nature and seriousness of these sensory needs.

How about this one? "Congratulations. Your child has met all the requirements for knowing how to use the bathroom. They know how to hit the toilet bowl, flush, put the seat down when done, and wash their hands. As a result of this level of proficiency your child is no longer needs or eligible for bathroom services."

Most would recognize this as an obvious logical disconnect. What does knowing how to use the bathroom have to do with the physical need to use the bathroom? Nothing. What does knowing how to grip a pencil, color within the lines, or use scissors have to do with the need to have sensory needs met? Nothing. Then why does a child that has demonstrated some proficiency in fine motor skills often lose the ability to have their physical sensory needs met? Another logical disconnect, yet it happens all the time.

We have all accepted that the physical human need of going to the bathroom is a reality of life. It must happen, and that is just the way it is. It is the same with sensory needs and autism. They are just a way of life, and should be incorporated into life. This does not mean that a child must always be in the occupational therapy room. There are many ways sensory needs can be met in the classroom, at home, in the car, or wherever they are. However, they must be recognized and met. Meeting the sensory needs of every autistic person should be seen as a way of life.

There is a responsibility when we are meeting sensory needs to meet the right need. If a child is giving all the signs of needing to go to the bathroom that parents and professionals have learned to recognize, what do we do? It's obvious isn't it? We offer them food! It is meeting a sensory need isn't it? What? Wrong need? We should encourage them go to the bathroom? Of course we should!

I was once conducting a classroom observation of a six-year-old, trying to help figure out what the problems were. At one point the child was refusing to do his work, and I could tell he needed sensory input, specifically motion. I told the people working with him he needed motion, so they applied deep pressure. I corrected them and told them again he needed motion. They provided more deep pressure.

At this point I called the boy over to me. I swung him up and down from the floor to over my head. His feet would hit the floor and he would say "up". After about fifteen times he didn't say up anymore, and I stopped. He gave me a hug, went back to his seat, and did his work. We don't fix motion needs by providing deep pressure, or any other legitimate sensory input. This is true for all sensory needs. Provide the right need at the right time. Just as when a child needs to go to the bathroom we don't fix that need by offering food. We save the food for when they are hungry.

If a child needs to go to the bathroom but they are not allowed, and they then begin to fall apart because their need is not being met, should they get in trouble? If the child then wets themselves are they oppositional and defiant? After all, they must have chosen to wet themselves to gain attention and cause problems.

Clearly this would not happen. The distress and resulting actions would be seen as a result of having the need to go to the bathroom. Yet, when autistic children who have physical sensory needs that are not being met fall apart they often get in trouble for inappropriate behavior. If they start to bounce, spin, pace, can't focus, or other "problem" behaviors they are often labeled oppositional and/or defiant. That is because the sensory needs of autism are not fully understood in the general population.

This misunderstanding is by no means limited to school settings – I have seen it in many places, including homes – and my apologies if the examples given seem biased. There are many great professionals in schools who understand and work with helping their autistic students meet these needs.

For the most part I assume that when sensory needs go unmet this is not because those around the autistic person are intentionally ignoring the need. Very few people in this world would do so. I encourage all those who support, are around, and are in the autism community to begin to think of sensory needs with autism in the same way as they think of the physical needs that all of humanity share. We all understand the need for things like going to the bathroom, food, water, and sleep. With autism, sensory management should be added to the list.

18. PERSEVERATION

Combat pilots have a term called target fixation. It is a problem. It is when a combat pilot is so focused on the enemy target that they lose situational awareness, which can result in them crashing into the enemy plane or hitting the ground. With autism we often experience a similar problem as we try to navigate through the problems of life. In autism circles it is called perseveration.

When a threat arises in the form of an enemy plane a pilot needs to eliminate that threat. They focus on the threat to solve the problem. When this focus becomes too great they forget some of the basics, like actually flying, and create a serious problem for themselves.

With autism we have problems that need to be eliminated too. Our target? "My computer is not working right." "We are out of chocolate ice-cream." "I can't find my favorite toy." "I texted a friend and they did not text back yet." The list of world-ending crises is seemingly endless.

When a person with autism becomes overly fixated, like the combat pilot, they lose situational awareness. The pilot forgets to pay attention to the basics of flying and crashes. The person on the spectrum forgets to pay attention to the basics of navigating life with autism, and crashes.

As previously discussed, with autism we cannot think and feel at the same time. When there is an unexpected problem that isn't instantly resolved there will likely be emotion. And when feeling emotion, proper thinking cannot happen. This results in two issues.

The first is that we lose the cognitive skill needed to actually solve the problem. Instead we are feeling emotions about our problem. This creates a self-feeding cycle that typically ends badly. Problem-solving skills are diminished due to feeling instead of thinking. The problem now appears larger as the skill needed to solve it is reduced. This generates an even greater amount of emotion, reducing the ability to solve the problem even further. This cycle often continues to spiral downward until the crash.

The second issue with perseveration is that we forget to stay on top of the skills needed to navigate in a world not set up for autism. We focus so much on the target that we forget to fly the plane, functioning properly in life with autism. Those around who see this happening try to intervene, but we shut them out, often getting angry with them. We tell them they don't understand how big the problem is, and that it needs to be fixed now! We are not listening to them try to explain that we are about to crash into our target, and/or hit the ground. We forgot to fly the plane.

Target fixation is a bigger problem for inexperienced pilots. A skilled pilot can tap into their experience base, recognize what is happening, and remember to fly the plane. Recognizing what is happening also keeps emotions in check. The "I've seen this before" experience helps keep perspective.

Experience and training makes a difference with autism too. When engaged in a crisis I try to remain detached enough to be able to recognize my own emotional involvement. I intellectually know that if I let emotions into the situation I will lose the capability to solve my problem. I will become overly fixated on my target. I will crash. I know I need to disengage, gain perspective, and come back later to solve my problem. I need to disengage from the target, and remember to fly the plane.

This is not always easy. With perseveration we tend to go a bit over the top.

I once spent three days driving over 100 miles to multiple stores to find the perfect stuffed animal for a kid. I had over a dozen lined up in my office, trying to decide which one to give to the child and which to return. I was out of control and I knew it. While I may have been fixated on my target, I was still able to somewhat fly the plane.

I'm picked on (jokingly) by a friend about the time I went to buy a stuffed animal horse for my office (apparently I have stuffed animal issues). I reached the point where I had given up on finding an acceptable horse in the store. My solution? I bought eight of them to examine at home to find the perfect one, and I would return the rest.

I tend to have better success with computer problems. After several "crash and burn" situations when I was younger, it is now easier for me to simply walk away and return later with a clearer mind and improved perspective.

Like most things with an upset and hostile autistic child, perseveration cannot be solved live. It is after the fact that perspective can be achieved, and plans made to hopefully not crash, or at least not as hard, next time.

Education and perspective make a difference. If the person on the autism spectrum and those supporting them can recognize this target fixation, this perseveration, it improves the odds of a successful outcome.

If the person is on the spectrum, they need to try to recognize the situation for what it is and disengage. Results will always be better later. If the autistic person can pay attention to those around them, remembering they are on their side, this can assist with perspective. While to the autistic person it may seem like nobody adequately understands the situation, those around them just might.

If we are supporting a person on the autism spectrum, we need to also recognize this kind of situation for what it is. Instead of being triggered ourselves by irrational snarling or being screamed at that we don't understand, just walk away. Yes, walk away. We can't help those who don't want help. Recognize the situation for what it is, and decide not to join in on the impending crash. If attempting to provide support is not welcome, our involvement will only escalate the problem. The situation is temporary. Walk away.

This target fixation, or perseveration, is a part of life with autism. At times it can be a good tool, like when it allows us to hyper focus and accomplish the impossible. Other times, like when the world seems like it's going to end because of something unimportant, I try to recognize it for what it is, and manage the situation, knowing it will soon pass.

Finishing off this chapter is a humorous look at when perseveration has gotten out of control for me personally, involving an unexpected rubber duck collection. How does someone end up with a collection of rubber ducks when they had absolutely no plan or intention of having a rubber duck collection? Welcome to autism.

It all started when I was getting toys and other items for my office. My favorite *Sesame Street* character as a kid was Ernie, and he had a rubber duck. I never had a rubber duck, and it seemed like a good opportunity. The only rubber duck I found was a pirate duck. I bought it, and was happy.

That is until I found the stereotypical plain no frills yellow rubber duck. It was the epitome of what a rubber duck should be. I bought it. I was then given a smaller camouflaged duck for my office to go with the other two. My two big ducks now had a kid. A nice rubber duck family. If only I had known.

While in Florida I visited a store with four different baby pirate ducks. I needed a baby pirate duck. It would make for a cute photo to go alongside an autism article, with the older and younger pirate ducks, and my camo duck could now have a younger sibling.

I could not decide which of the four baby pirate ducks I wanted. They were cheap. So I bought all four. Yes, this was the first sign of impending trouble. Had I forced myself to be decisive, and buy only one duck (or none?), I might not be telling this story.

This same trip I saw a three pack of rubber ducks. It was a mother and two tiny yellow baby ducks, even smaller than my baby pirate ducks. Of course, I got them. My duck family was now complete, with a few leftover ducks. I should have seen this coming. I didn't.

My next Florida trip I found a whole bunch of different small rubber ducks, mostly career-oriented. I envisioned different photo scenarios for articles. I bought a firefighter duck, a police duck, a train engineer duck, a sheriff duck, and for something overtly female, a princess duck.

At this point I knew I had lost control. I had just bought the rubber duck version of the Village People to add to the family. We were now beyond the rubber duck *Brady Bunch* stage. We were at the rubber duck equivalent of *Cheaper by the Dozen*.

I had to admit with some embarrassment that I had rubber duck collection. "Hi, my name is Paul, and I'm a rubber duck-aholic." I assumed there were recovery groups for everything, but I was unable to find a local chapter of "Rubber Ducks Anonymous".

I promptly bought a yellow chicken to hang out with all my rubber ducks. (See what great control I have. I did not buy a rubber duck. It's a chicken.) The rubber chicken was to illustrate being different, because it sort of looks like all the ducks, but is not a duck. And in my defense the rubber chicken has proved to be very valuable in the office, and is also featured on the cover of this book.

I have continued to buy ducks. Party ducks. Holiday ducks. Ducks wearing all sorts of different outfits. Every duck has had a reason. I won't buy just any duck. I need to like the duck. I have also made rules for myself. For example, rubber ducks are yellow. A little autism-based rule orientation can be a good thing.

The yellow duck rule lasted until "super duck" who was blue. Super duck technically didn't break the rule. Super duck is really yellow when in normal rubber duck life, and puts on its blue outfit to fight crime. So it is really a yellow duck under the blue outfit. (Yes, I am rationalizing now. Is this the rubber duck equivalent of going to a bar and saying I will only have one drink?)

I know my yellow duck exception doesn't apply to the purple party duck, the purple duck wearing a raincoat, or my red and pink love ducks. Precedent was set. Besides, I can't have a zebra duck that is yellow. (Honestly. I don't have a problem. I could stop at any time.)

I have still managed to abide by my rule that I am not allowed to buy rubber ducks online. Bookmakers in Vegas have been crunching the numbers on that one ever since I first saved links for ducks I'd like to buy online, but I can't because I don't buy ducks online.

The one rule I really will not break is that ducks are not allowed to squeak. Sensory trumps all. I suppose I could learn how to de-squeak a duck. I'm going to try and not go there.

The sad news is I could have told a very similar story with hand-blown reproduction Eighteenth Century glassware, from P&B Glass. It all started with a wonderful blue goblet. If anyone would like a great deal on a hand blown punch-bowl, some glasses, and a few odds and ends please let me know. I'd like some of that square footage back in my house.

I keep telling myself that rubber ducks are cheap and easy to store. So far, eighty one ducks ... and a chicken.

PART C

BRIDGING THE GAP

19. LIFE ISN'T FAIR

"Sometimes life isn't fair."

- My mom

As a kid I don't know how many thousands of times my mom told me that life wasn't fair. When she said it I would be expected to get over whatever the issue was and move on. She didn't want to hear about it, and wouldn't entertain me by listening. Whenever this happened the problem wasn't anything that really mattered in life. My complaints were things like my sister had crossed the center line in the back seat of the car, or that somebody had gotten a bigger piece of cake.

With autism we are big on the concept that things should be fair, not just for us, but for everyone. My mom did me a huge favor by making me understand the world was not fair, and that if I expected it to be, or exhausted myself arguing about nonsense, that things would not go well for me – in the short term with her, and in the long term in life.

In this chapter I am certainly not trying to say that there should not be services, supports, and other help provided to people on the autism spectrum. Nothing could be further from the truth. We all often need help, and especially those who – for lack of a better term – are "low functioning" would not be able to survive or thrive without outside assistance. What I am talking about is an attitude.

I see a cross section of the autism community that thinks the world owes them something because they are autistic. I am not talking about needing help. I am talking about an attitude of entitlement, often combined with no willingness to learn, grow, or adapt. The world is what it is, and will not change for us. We are in the minority, and the majority makes the cultural rules the game is played by. The world owes us nothing because of our autism diagnosis.

My attitude is that if someone attempts to understand me, or accommodate me, I am immensely grateful for their act of kindness. They owe me nothing, but have shown me patience and understanding, and attempted to make my life better. That is not my right. That is their gift.

If we were to talk to any group of people in the world I am guessing we would discover that every person in the group had endured some type of hardship in their life. Some people have certainly endured more than others, and many hide it well, but suffering of some sort is common to us all. Some have better lives than we do, and some have worse lives. Life is not fair. The difference with autism is that our life difficulties are likely to be in different categories than most of the population. Where we typically struggle are the areas of life most others view as simple.

I do not view my role as an autism professional to give someone a good or easy life. My role is to instead give someone the skills they need to thrive despite the difficult circumstances life will bring them.

There is this twisted idea in much of American culture that we are supposed to be happy all the time, and that if we are not there is something wrong with us. This idea is distinctly American, and distinctly post World War II. It isn't seen in most places in the world (though it is spreading) and wasn't really found prior to the war. I view it as a cultural flaw because it does not reflect reality and does harm. Life is difficult, and suffering is universal. This does not mean life cannot be good or rewarding, because it can. It does mean a perpetual state of happiness without struggle is a fantasy.

I am sure there are a few people that are having a hard time with the idea that hardship is inescapable. These people will probably want to burn me at the stake for this next one. That is that suffering and hardship serve a useful and productive role in life.

When I think of someone who has never had to suffer, accept responsibility, or endure doing the hard thing in life, the image that comes to mind isn't good. We end up with a biological adult with the stability, life skills, and maturity of a three-year-old. Is that what we really want for anyone?

It is my contention that hardship and suffering is the only way we grow and mature as human beings. This is how we learn patience. This is how we learn to persevere and solve difficult problems. This is how we realize what is really important in life.

When we go through a hard time in life who do we generally seek out? As a middle-aged adult do we go to the local college to talk with a young student for wisdom? Do we look to the "perfect people" in the world who have had a reasonably easy, smooth, and gifted life for advice? No. I go looking for an older, more mature, battle-hardened veteran of life. I want someone who has struggled, fought, suffered anguish, been there and back again, and come out the other side in one piece, and a stronger, better human being because of it.

Like most people I have gone through some miserable, hard, difficult times in life. They are experiences I would not wish on anyone. (Okay, there are a few I might wish it on.) I never want to go through anything like those experiences again in my life. At the time I would have given anything to be able to escape the suffering I was going through. However, I am glad those experiences happened. They have made me who I am, and I am a tougher, smarter, more mature person because of them.

No matter who we are, the goal is to learn and grow from the tough times in life. These times will be there whether we like it or not. Life is not fair. The sooner we can accept this difficult idea the better. We have a choice. We can be crushed by the hard times, or we can harness an otherwise miserable experience to make ourselves or our children better people.

Again, I am not saying there should not be services for those on the autism spectrum. We all need help, and many need that help to truly live and survive. My concern is an attitude I see with some on the spectrum who demand the world change for them. The world is what it is, and we need to live in it as it is. Unfair? Maybe, but as my mom kept telling me: "Sometimes life isn't fair."

20. BE OPEN

"That is not a duck."

- Multiple

In my office I have a line of rubber ducks – part of the rubber duck collection. In the middle of the line sits the rubber chicken, which is in the same style as a typical rubber duck. It is the same chicken seen on the cover of this book. I have had several people in my office see the chicken and stop mid-sentence saying: "That is not a duck!" This is exactly why I bought the chicken. It is not a duck, and I have a point to make.

I illustrate the world as a duck pond filled with rubber ducks. Those of us on the autism spectrum are the chicken. The chicken is sort of like a duck. The chicken can pretend it is a duck. However, everyone looks at it and says: "That is not a duck!"

Ducks swim, quack, waddle, and give it absolutely no thought. They are ducks. It is what they do. The worst duck will do these things far better than the most skilled, hardest working chicken trying to look like a duck. A chicken that can manage to keep its beak above water, give a sad little half quack, and sort of waddle in line is really impressive for a chicken. It is really sad for a duck.

I will sometimes try to convince kids that my little chicken is a duck. None of them buy it. On the autism spectrum we as chickens can insist to all the ducks around us that we are just another duck, and pretend to be a duck. It doesn't work. Even the most skilled and experienced of us with autism are distinctly different, and the world has no trouble saying: "That is not a duck!" This leads us to a choice. We can be a bad duck, or we can be a good chicken. My vote is for good chicken.

I try to help those I work with to embrace who they are. They are on the autism spectrum learning to function in a world not set up for autism. With autism we are in the minority and do not get to make the rules for how the world works. We are the chicken living in the duck pond.

Those who become the most successful chickens living in the duck pond will willingly say: "Yes I am a chicken, and that makes it tough to swim and quack, but let me show you what I can do because I am a chicken." Or with autism say: "Yes I am on the autism spectrum, and that poses some challenges living in a world where most people are not like me. But, I am okay with that, and offer a lot to the world by being true to who I am."

Instead of trying to be a bad duck, pretending everything is fine as we are struggling to keep our beak above water, we should be true to who we are and be a really great chicken, and not try be like everyone else. It is by viewing the world differently, and embracing that unique perspective, that we can be successful chickens and make a difference in the duck pond.

To be a successful chicken in the duck pond we need to be willing to be open and public about being on the autism spectrum. If we try to hide it we will not be successful. All the ducks know we are not a duck. We might as well be okay with the idea and seek their assistance in living in the duck pond as a really good chicken.

I tell the people wrestling with this idea that everyone already knows they are different; they make social, interpersonal, and cultural errors. So do I. I have been working on these skills for decades and am a professional in the autism business. But I'm not flawless. Unless my contact with someone is very short and superficial everyone can tell I am different. If I'm having a bad day, it is even worse. I have a choice. I can be an awkward, geeky jerk, or I can be autistic. I choose autistic.

When someone from another country is among us we give them the benefit of the doubt when they make cultural errors. They are not in their own culture. We presume there was no ill intent, and that the mistakes are from ignorance rather than malice. People think when those of us on the autism spectrum are out in the world that we are in our own culture. We are not. Our culture is autism, but nobody knows that. So they presume that when we make mistakes it is with intent and malice. There is no benefit of the doubt given, because almost every five-year-old knows how to properly handle the situation that we messed up.

By being public with our being on the autism spectrum, we are given, even by the casual observer, the benefit of the doubt. Our error was not likely with intent. We still need to own what we did, and fix what we broke, but an understanding that the error was without intent allows us to be more successful in life.

I'd rather be a good chicken than a bad duck.

21. INTELLECT NOT INSTINCT

I was shocked to find out that most non-autistic people operate on instinct. They go with what feels right, even with major decisions. If an autistic person attempted to live life on instinct and what felt right they would be a squirrel on the highway of life. Survival would be unlikely, and if they did survive it would be by pure dumb luck. A successful life with autism requires the person on the autism spectrum to control their instinctive responses and instead replace them with an intellectual, analyzed response.

Some may say this is not fair. People should be free to be who they are and others in society should adapt. Even if this is the way it ought to be, this is not the way it is. The world needs to be viewed as it actually is by those on the spectrum, no matter how unfair. We are free to be who we want to be in the privacy of our own homes. I encourage it, and do the same. When in public we need to operate by the rules of the world for success.

If a person gets on an airplane and flies to a distant country they are aware they are crossing into a different culture, and those in the foreign country are also aware that person is from a different culture. A person on the autism spectrum crosses cultural lines every time they walk out their front door, or even when doing something as simple as sending a text message. They are not always aware they are entering a cross-cultural experience, and everyone else is almost never aware the autistic person is attempting to function in a culture not their own.

That does not mean cross-cultural skills cannot be learned or even mastered. Think of the act of driving a car. There is nothing innately natural or instinctive about it. It is a learned activity. Most have watched someone else drive for many years before being allowed to attempt it, reinforced by minimum legal driving ages. Before driving someone studies what must be done. They are then slowly trained step by step by an experienced driver, often a professional whose career is specifically teaching this unnatural act of driving a car. Eventually, given enough time and practice the new driver is awarded a license and given legal permission to drive alone. This does not mean they are any good at it. New drivers often make a lot of mistakes, with a high incidence of accidents. They need to actively use their intellect and actively think about braking, acceleration, turning, and so on. Given years of experience, many – but certainly not all – begin to function automatically when driving. The foot automatically hits the brake and the hands automatically steer the wheel. It becomes an instinctive response. But it is a trained instinctive response rather than a natural one.

Even at an advanced stage driving is not necessarily fully automatic. Given poor visibility, poor road conditions, heavy traffic, and/or distractions, driving requires much more conscious effort, and mistakes are made. As someone reaches an advanced age, is tired, or ill, again, driving requires even more effort and more mistakes are made. All this is because driving is not naturally instinctive. I am a skilled experienced driver who has never had an at-fault accident. Handling an intersection with a stop sign most days requires little conscious thought, even with other cars around. Yet there have been days where I have sat waiting for the stop sign to turn green (spoiler alert: it never does).

All of the above work of learning a skill like driving is true for the autistic individual learning to navigate life. While I am a skilled and experienced person, the average non-autistic five-year-old has better natural interpersonal and cultural instincts than I do. My functioning in life is like driving. It is a learned process, and while I can get very good through study and many years of experience, it is learned with all the flaws of an unnatural learned process.

I have had people tell me they don't want to learn how to operate in life intellectually because they do not want to change who they are, or pretend to be someone they are not. However, when functioning intellectually in public life we are not being fake. We are being who we really are, but communicating that message in a language that is understood by those who are not autistic. We are translating ourselves into their language, as best we can, so that the message is properly delivered. It is not being fake. It is communicating effectively.

Functioning in life intellectually means we will never be perfect, like a driver is never perfect. There will be good days, and bad. There will be days the conditions are so bad that we don't go out, just like many drivers don't go out in a blizzard. There will be days we have the autistic equivalent of waiting for a stop sign to turn green. Life can and will sometimes be messy. However, overall, we can be competent and skilled. It will be a learned instinct like driving: not flawless, but still pretty good.

22. AVOIDING AUTISM-BASED PROBLEMS

In my office I illustrate controlling the autistic instinctive response with a toy car and a rubber duck. The car represents a person living their life. The duck represents the autism-based problem. The duck is in the path of the car. The sooner we see the duck while driving the car, the easier it will be to not hit the duck.

At a distance it takes a minor adjustment for the car to miss the duck. The closer the car is to the duck the harder we have to turn the wheel to miss it. More work is involved, and the risks are greater. If uncorrected, our car will reach a point of no return, where it is impossible to not hit the duck. The sooner we can recognize we are heading toward the duck the easier it is to correct course and miss our feathered friend.

I ask people how soon they are able to see that they are heading towards a duck in their life, or if they can tell they are approaching an autism-caused problem. I regularly hear that they don't even realize they've hit a duck until long after it is over. Using our duck metaphor this means not seeing the duck coming in the road, or even the poof of feathers as it bounces off the windshield; the car is back in the garage, and crows have picked the scene clean before there is recognition of the problem. So how do we help with this?

The first step is knowing what a duck looks like. Obviously we are not talking about a literal duck, but the areas of our lives where autism causes problems. How do we learn this? It is through the study of autism, looking at patterns of problems in the history of our lives, and with the help of the non-autistic around us.

This book can help someone learn and understand some of the autistic instinctive responses, as well as how to manage them. The better we know our vulnerabilities and how we are likely to function in the world, the more successful we can be. We may be able to identify a duck in the road early enough to miss it.

Also, all of us have our own individual patterns of weaknesses and vulnerability in life. If I know I have a pattern of making certain types of errors, it can help to identify when another might be approaching. At an instinctive level I may not be aware of the duck in the road, but intellectually I am aware that I should be looking for one and what it might look like.

For example, if someone has a pattern of sharing too much deep personal information in casual settings they will likely have had times of driving people away due to appearing too interpersonally needy, or having that information used against them by people they should not have trusted. This is a common autism related scenario. By recognizing this pattern in their life someone on the autism spectrum can see their own potential for over sharing information in wrong settings, and take appropriate steps to make sure the depth of their communication matches the depth of the relationship.

The non-autistic around us can help to identify potential incoming problems. They can do this with us live as we are going through our day, as well as help us identify the patterns in life where potential problems lie. If they know us well, they will know where our ducks in the road are.

To help us avoid hitting the ducks in the road, just as with a real car and a real duck, there is a benefit to slowing down. The more ducks there are, and the worse the travel conditions, the slower we should go.

Often people on the autism spectrum go through life as if they are in a race car driving along a wide, straight, and empty road in perfect weather. "Full speed ahead!" With this lack of caution, there are ducks bouncing off the car all over the place – there are lots of problems. By slowing ourselves down we improve our odds of missing the ducks.

When we enter a new situation we should not race in. Be quiet. Hang out on the edges and observe. Study and determine where the ducks might be hiding. Even in familiar situations where we think we know where all the problems are, our odds are better by slowing ourselves down a little. There may be a new duck or two that has waddled into the road. The more ducks that can be found and avoided as we go through life the better off we are.

I have made the decision to slow down. One example of this is with things such as humor, especially online. There is too much that can go wrong. The number of times I think of something I consider funny and want to post – but don't – is incredible. When thinking something is funny I might be right nine out of ten times, or even ninety nine out of one hundred, but the consequences of getting it wrong are too high. I'd rather someone consider me boring than a jerk.

I have reached the point in life where if I know there is a potential duck in the road I'm pretty good at not hitting the duck. My problem is when I relax and mistakenly start to act on instinct again that I forget to look for ducks. Suddenly there is a poof of feathers and I realize too late that I have messed up. I can't relax – I need to be ever vigilant.

All the social training and knowledge of what we should be actively doing is pointless unless we can successfully miss the ducks.

23. THREE STAGES OF ACTION

So, we now have a plan to try to avoid autism-based problems, to see the ducks on the road. But just seeing and not hitting ducks is only part of the solution. How can we on the autism spectrum actually function well in life? We are people with goals, jobs, relationships, and so on. How do we navigate all that?

A lot of professionals out there working with autism are teaching someone what to say and do in certain situations. And there is some value to that, but the problem is that all situations are different, and culture changes with time and location. This means that what used to be appropriate may no longer continue to be appropriate, or what was appropriate in one location may not be in another. The skill or knowledge is not necessarily transferable. What is covered in social skills books or classes may not always work. My method is slower, but better. It involves teaching someone the skills to study the cultures around them, learning, and continually making adjustments. It is teaching them how to fish, rather than giving them a fish.

Growing up I developed a three-stage process for improving success in social encounters. I still use this process today. This process closely resembles the three stages that a military unit, sports team, or business team would use. They are: planning, engagement, and debriefing.

Planning

Many people understand and use the first step of this three-stage process. The planning. We do research, try to anticipate what is coming, and prepare ourselves ahead of time for what we think we will encounter. With autism the amount of time and energy that goes into planning can be staggering. This is partly about avoiding ducks, but equally part of planning proactively for what we will be doing.

What is the social venue like? How many people will be there? Sensory problems? Specifically who will we be interacting with? What type of relationship do I have with each of these people? What are the rules for each of those types of relationships? What are the patterns of normal for each of the people I plan to interact with to establish a baseline? What topics will I interact with each person about? Scripting conversations, and multiple variables to the scripts. What potentially socially awkward moments may happen, and when, and how will I respond? How do I dress? How do I carry myself? Contingency problems: nearest acceptable food, bathrooms, medical help, clothing changes. It goes on and on.

This isn't just the major encounters such as parties, meetings, and things non-autistic people think of as social engagements. This is every situation. It can be as simple as trying to buy something, take a walk around the block, or make a phone call.

Because of the amount of work involved an autistic person may not be up to it at any given moment. Personal costs need to be considered. I describe life with autism as a cup of pennies, and when we are out of pennies our day is over. There is no such thing as a free lunch – everything costs something. As a result we do a lot of resource management. Every decision is a cost benefit analysis. "What does it cost me, and what do I get out of it?" As a result, no matter how well we plan we may decide last minute that something fails the cost benefit analysis. We end up cancelling. It isn't that we don't want to do something; it's that that we need to survive.

Engagement

Stage two is the actual social encounter. There is a well-known military saying that "No battle plan survives contact with the enemy". With our social engagements this military adage often holds true. We have made plans about what to expect, and how we will interact. When we encounter real people, and attempt to pull this off in real time, our plans and expectations often start to fall apart.

While engaged with others we try to stick to our plans. Intense focus is on trying to control our instinctive responses that would result in saying or doing something inappropriate. Watch for ducks. Every word, every gesture, every decision, needs to be consciously analyzed. Especially in the early learning stages of this technique we may appear awkward, stiff, and not quite right.

The problem? Other people are behaving on instinct. They do not know our plans. They have not read our scripts. They may behave differently than expected. This can cause the autistic person to be overwhelmed and panic. Panic is an emotion, and autistic people do not think well with emotion. In panic we hit ducks.

A real-time solution that often works is to go quiet. Remember the idea of slowing down to miss ducks. We withdraw a little bit (figuratively and/or literally), and observe. Many have learned to do this naturally.

This gives us the opportunity to manage emotions, study and learn, and possibly re-engage. It is survival. If the situation is too much it may even mean leaving entirely. It is better to walk out than to crash and burn.

Over time, this three-stage process should reduce these awkward or negative experiences as there continues to be learning and growth. Which brings us to what may be the most important and neglected of the three stages.

Debriefing

The third stage is debriefing. This happens after every military action, sporting event, or even many first dates. This debriefing stage is likely the most important of the three stages. It is also the stage most often neglected as we attempt to be more successful.

What went well? Were there any surprises? What did not go well? Things that went well, could they have been better? Could there be any signals that were being sent to me that I missed? Did my non-verbal and verbal messages match each other and the situation? Was my interaction appropriately reciprocal? Did I adequately consider others' feelings? Did I break any cultural rules? If so, what, and how badly? And so on, as the analysis continues.

The purpose of this debriefing is not to make us feel bad. It serves a critical role in both the short term and the long term. Due to impaired theory of mind skills (the ability to instinctively understand the perspective and feelings of others) we need to do this process at the intellectual level.

Short-term debriefing is focused on if there anything I need to go fix. Do I need to engage any relationship rescue techniques? Do I owe any apologies, explanations, or need to give/seek clarifications?

No matter how good we may be, with autism we say things we should not say, and we do things we should not do. We do not mean to hurt people and damage relationships, but it happens anyway. We do not want to make excuses for our errors to other people. We need to own the issues. It is an opportunity to try to put right what we may have made wrong.

Long term, this debriefing process is how we learn. It gives us what we need to be able to better prepare ourselves for the next social encounter. Every debriefing is really an early part of the next planning phase. We now have newer and better information than before. It is not just theoretical, but based on real life experience. It improves the odds of better planning.

Be aware, kids will likely need help working through the process. This is also true for anyone new to the technique. Even having done this as a matter of routine for decades, I still seek insight from non-autistic people I trust with things I can't figure out. No one is an expert at everything and, being autistic, by definition I struggle in this area just like the kids I work with, only to a differing degree.

Too Much

Analysis at the level described may be overwhelming. Start small and simple. Choose one thing. The types of areas to start should be the struggles in life that are causing us the most problems, or the issues that are the easiest to fix. Both of these will give us the greatest immediate benefit. One addresses our greatest problems, providing biggest impact. The other uses the least resources for success. Ultimately there is no bad place to start.

Go through the three-step process using that one new piece of information. If too much is attempted all at once nothing will be accomplished. When we are confident using the first piece of information we then add a second, eventually a third, and so on. Over time, skills and abilities will continue to grow. Success breeds more success.

Progress is incremental and perpetual. There is no point where we can say we have "arrived" and stop. We can always get better. Culture and social rules are always evolving. What I am describing is a way of approaching life. We have autism-based instincts in a non-autism-based world. That does not change. We will always need to use intellect over instinct.

24. RESEARCH AND DECISION-MAKING

If we are going to use our intellect rather than our instincts to interact with the world there needs to be information to use. This involves research and study. We need information about: people, relationships, emotions, body language, culture, and almost any aspect of human life you could think of. Without reliable and useful information we would be in as much trouble as if we went with our instincts.

Autism Specific

One way to do this is to read information written specifically for people on the autism spectrum. I'm not going to say never do this, but it is not one of my favorites, and I think it has problems. One of my issues is that these books tend to be written by experts in autism rather than experts in whatever the topic is they are writing about. They do serve a purpose, especially for those just starting out, but the information will often be limited and simplistic. That is fine as a starting place, but if an autistic person doesn't move beyond these materials it will be hard to be successful.

Direct Observation

One excellent method of gaining useable information is direct observation. For every single location out there the rules will be slightly different. What is worn. What is thought funny. What is talked about. How outgoing and expressive people are. The list of what can make each tiny subculture unique is nearly endless. This is also information that can never be gotten from a book or other resources. The way we find out is to go, err on the side of caution with all decisions, slow ourselves down, keep our mouths shut, and do research. We should also do this with online communities and every other situation we walk into.

One thing I do with direct observation is establish patterns within a person or a situation, and a range of what is typical. If I am trying to fit in, I then know where to target my decisions. There is not one exact right answer of how to dress, or anything else. It will fall into a bell curve with outliers on both ends of the range, and most in the middle. We can then make our decisions about where within that range we fit and are most comfortable.

Once I have established patterns I look for breaks in the patterns. So for example, if someone is typically loud and outgoing, and when I interact with them they are loud and outgoing, my work is easy. They fit their own pattern. If someone who is typically loud is all of a sudden quiet and withdrawn, that breaks their personal pattern. A mental red flag goes up that something is different and I need to figure out what caused the pattern to change. Similarly, if someone who typically dresses very casually dresses more formally on this occasion, the pattern is broken and I want to investigate what changed. The range of things to find patterns in within a person or a situation can be nearly endless. The more we analyze, pattern, and track, the more successful we can be.

Specialty Materials

These days there are self-help materials out there for almost every topic. These can be books, magazine articles, online articles, television shows, video clips, and many other sources. Subjects include: body language, making friends, generational differences, cross-cultural adjustment, rules for online communication, making winning arguments, dealing with bosses and coworkers, how to get a job, how to get promoted, establishing life priorities, and a seemingly never-ending list of others. These materials are not written by autism experts, but are written by experts in their fields. They are also not written for people on the autism spectrum, but written for everyone. These resources are more thorough and detailed than what would generally be written specifically for an autistic audience. These types of materials can help us improve what we do, as well as understand why other people do what they do.

Indirect Materials

Like specialty materials, these can be: books, magazine articles, online articles, television shows, video clips, and many other sources. This is a more advanced method of gaining information, and tends to be used by people who have been doing this for a while. Indirect materials are harder to learn from, but may contain subtle hidden information that cannot be found in other places. While there may be informational value to the direct message the author is putting out there as the topic that is good for general knowledge and intelligence, what is being sought by us for interpersonal and cultural success is not directly addressed.

What does what the author is saying tell me about the author's: experience, biases, goals, perspective or the intended audience? Why does someone think this needs to be said? Are they right or wrong, and why? It is the hidden stuff. It may be books or articles on things as diverse as: sports commentary, internet security, television ratings, body decomposition, Robert E. Lee, classic rock, crafting, what it is like to be performing on Broadway, and so on. It can even be as bizarre as thinking about why a product or package was designed the way it was, and what that tells us about the designer and intended user. We can gain direct knowledge, but also the indirect hidden stuff that gives us insights into people and culture.

Cultural Litter

When I think of cultural litter I am talking about stuff that has little to no redeeming value on its own. It is fluffy or biased opinion pieces, pop culture material, clickbait articles, social media posts and comments, memes, and even things like advertisements and restaurant menus. It is all the meaningless, ulterior motive, money-making, attention-grabbing stuff that litters our physical and electronic lives. Sometimes it is entertaining. Sometimes it is a necessary part of living life and functioning. Sometimes it is purely the garbage and cultural white noise surrounding us that we would love to be able to get rid of.

This type of material is actually easier to study for hidden information because the information that we are looking for is less hidden. The raw content of the material is often biased, wrong, or meaningless. It is so blatant that the reverse engineering of the author's perspective and the intended audience is easier.

While we may not seek out this cultural litter, it is all around us, and we may as well learn what we can from it about people and culture. Just don't make the mistake of believing the direct content is necessarily correct. Believe instead the hidden indirect content.

Putting it all Together

Any one piece of information, whether directly told or indirectly figured out, may or may not be correct. Just as when doing research on anything, never trust only one source, and recognize that some sources are better than others. In insurance there is a concept called the law of large numbers. This is the idea that with any one situation there is a limited ability to accurately predict an outcome. However, given a large number of situations to analyze, reliable patterns and data can be concluded. The same is true here. Even if we like one piece of information, we have no way of determining its reliability. However, if we see the same patterns of information coming up over and over again from multiple sources, and when cross referencing different types of sources, we can have greater confidence in the use of what we have learned.

With the patterns of information we are gleaning from multiple sources, there will likely be a range of what is typical, as discussed in the "Direct Observation" section above: outliers on both ends, with the majority in the middle, just like with a bell curve. We want to be able to be ourselves, and not be a cookie-cutter representation of everything and everyone around us. It is individuality and diversity that makes each of us who we are, autistic or not. However, there are factors regarding diversity and our decisions that can come into play which will impact our overall success.

Think of it like this: each person has up to one hundred points they can spend on diversity and individuality while remaining within cultural and societal boundaries for any given situation. Someone who spends no points on diversity is the most typical, least risk-taking, most boring person in the room. There is nothing edgy about them, and equally there is nothing interesting about them either. The higher the number of diversity points someone uses towards the hundred point threshold, the more individualistic, creative, and interesting they are. However, if someone crosses that hundred point threshold they then are seen as inappropriate, offensive, and unsuccessful. The further someone goes past the hundred point threshold the worse it becomes.

Everything that separates us from the center of a bell curve uses some of those one hundred points. The further we get from the center of the bell curve the more points each difference costs us. A minor difference costs little. A more significant difference costs more. If making a decision to be different in a way that crosses outside the range of the bell curve entirely that single decision becomes very costly. Depending on what it is, one such decision could by itself use most of our allowed hundred points, and could even be so bad that it totally busts the budget and makes us seem completely unacceptable and inappropriate.

For example: showing up to a formal wedding in a dark suit, dress shirt, and tie, is center bell curve. It costs us nothing. Showing up with a wild tie, or no suit coat, would make us slightly different, but comfortably within the bell curve range. We would use up some of the hundred points, but not many. Showing up in shorts and a casual shirt would by itself put us well outside the bell curve range, but if everything else about us was perfect we may not cross the hundred point threshold. Showing up to the wedding in pajamas and a bathrobe would likely all by itself exceed the hundred point threshold, and we would be viewed as offensive and inappropriate, even if everything else about us was flawless.

To be successful, the more we diverge from the norm in one area, the more we need to fit within the norm in other areas. We can be different and remain individuals, but there is such a thing as being too different and too individual, crossing the line into where we have a problem. With autism, we tend to do that a lot.

My recommendation for success is to imagine that, if everyone else has one hundred points of individuality and freedom to be different, we ourselves only have fifty. Not fair? Maybe, but remember, life isn't fair.

Why do I set this lower threshold for those of us who are autistic? Because we are using points we don't know we are using. With autism we are a bit odd and quirky to begin with. We may not see it ourselves, but trust me it is there. We just don't fit. Our oddness and quirkiness will use up a good chunk of points that others don't use, and that we don't know we are using. The other reason I suggest limiting ourselves to fifty diversity points when everyone else gets one hundred is that we will not be good at judging how many points each decision to be different from the norm costs us. We may think a decision is typical, or a minor departure, when in reality it is a more significant departure from the norm, costing us more points than we realize.

All that being said – about doing research, finding norms, and fitting in – there are times we should never compromise on what we do or say. We should be willing to compromise on culture, and do so all the time. We should never be willing to compromise on things like values, beliefs, and priorities. These are what make us who we are and should not be compromised, regardless of the bell curve of the room we have walked into. We are now dealing with moral and ethical issues. If our morals and ethics don't fit the situation we find ourselves in, it may be the first clue that we don't belong there, and that it is time to leave.

25. PROTECT ME FROM ME

With autism there are many factors that can cause us to have difficulty processing social or other information effectively when we need to do so in real time. Things like emotions, processing speed, and working memory are a few common autism oriented factors of the many which can interfere. As a result, mistakes are made. To help with this I make a plan ahead of time for what I will do given certain circumstances. Essentially these are rules for navigating life. I trust myself more than anyone else, and I make all my own decisions. The difference is I am not making them live. I am making as many decisions as I can ahead of time when I am at my best to do so. I can then use emotionless logic. All I need to do is recognize the patterns of a situation, and remember what I have already decided for those patterns. Why? Because I need to protect me from me.

Many who are not autistic make rules to protect themselves, though to a much lesser extent. They will not drink and drive. They will not go to bed angry. They will wait to spend money over a certain amount. I have just taken it to the next level by deciding absolutely everything I can ahead of time. This protects me in three large categories of life.

Everyday Life

The decision to use intellect over instinct with autism prepares us to navigate in a culture that is not our own. There can be so many decisions that need to be made instantly throughout the day that the processing can slow things down. We are deciding what we are going to do in every area of cultural difference. Our instincts will serve us poorly, so we need to be able to intellectually analyze and make decisions in less than a second.

For example, we know that telling the boss's boss that their idea is stupid is not in our best interests, and should not be said in a non-autism culture. By deciding ahead of time that when a stupid idea is presented, which is not an immediate life or death issue, we will stay silent, unless personally asked a direct question about the idea. If asked a direct question will respond that we would like more time to think about the situation. This is making a decision ahead of time to protect me from me. We have not lied or broken any ethical or autism-based rule. We have sidestepped a problem.

I know that I don't know how to properly dress for every social situation. By having already decided that I will do what research I can, and then err on the side of more formal or cautious clothing choices, I am avoiding potential offense or impropriety.

I know that my sense of humor may not fit all people or situations. I have decided ahead of time that it is better to be considered boring than a jerk. By having already decided to not use humor on social media or any public written communication I am protecting myself from the percentage of times that misplaced humor will cause offense.

I have likely made several thousand such pre-decisions. The more I can pre-decide the more successful I will be. While the thought of thousands of decisions is likely overwhelming, realize that I have been doing this for several decades. Start with one. Got that down? Add a second. Then over time the list will build. Good places to start are the areas that can have the greatest negative consequences: bad days, and personally vulnerable areas.

Bad Day

I specifically have rules to protect me from me when I am having a bad day. When I recognize I'm having a bad day due to anxiety, illness, exhaustion, sensory problems, or other factors I know I am fighting an emotional response. When functioning with emotional issues I know my likelihood of making critical mistakes goes up dramatically. As a result, knowing the areas I am vulnerable in when having a bad day, I trigger the bad day rules to protect me from me. Having already decided these rules ahead of time, and trusting myself when I am thinking clearly, I can avoid case-by-case processing in the moment.

An example of a rule in this category would be that I will not allow myself to respond to any form of communication until at least the next day. No phone calls, emails, text messages, and so on. I am concerned I am going to say something I actually mean but is better left unsaid, or if it should be said needs to be translated into non-autism-friendly terms. Another example of a bad day rule is I will not let myself make any major decisions until at least the next day. I also cannot spend money over a relatively small amount. Everything is oriented towards protecting me from me.

Vulnerable Areas

In each person's life there are areas where we as individuals are vulnerable. These areas will be made up of the unique history, triggers, temptations, and shortcomings of each of us that make us who we are. Every person will have a slightly different list.

An example of this in my life is alcohol. I never touched alcohol until my late thirties, and started then for medical reasons, due to extreme sensitivities to depressants. I recognized the need to develop some resistance for safety. I knew with autism that I don't do anything halfway, and so would make a phenomenal alcoholic. Therefore I put in place rules to protect me from me. I would only allow myself one drink in a twenty four hour period. I would only drink when at home and not going somewhere. If I ever felt like I needed a drink, I would not allow myself to have one, because then I would not be drinking, but self-medicating.

Another example of this in my life is more autism-based. I know I can be a bit obsessive. Based on having made mistakes in this area in the past I decided on the rule that I would only ever make three attempts to contact someone without a response, and if they still didn't respond I would not attempt to contact that person again. The three attempts cover all forms of contact, and there is no time limit. This avoids my overdoing attempts to contact, and forces me to be thoughtful and careful when I do attempt contact, because I only have three opportunities.

I encourage others to follow the same path I have. Trust yourself with deciding ahead of time as many decision in your life as possible, especially in areas of vulnerability or where there are patterns of having problems. It is not being fake. It is being prepared.

26. TRAUMA: HOW HARD TO PUSH

What happens when a person is pushed past their breaking point? We begin to tap into reserves that are truly there for life and death type situations. To access these reserves creates trauma. Someone isn't stretched anymore – they are broken and damaged.

People may have heard in movies about a military pilot pushing a jet engine beyond 100%, say to 105% or 110%. That actually can be done, but comes with severe consequences. On a jet engine the 100% threshold is not the most the engine can do. It is the most the engine can do without causing damage to itself. If it is life or death the pilot is able to push the engine farther than that. When they land, the engine will be thrown away.

A person on the autism spectrum can find themselves in a situation beyond their capabilities, and they carry on anyway. They are pushed beyond the 100% threshold. Damage is done. The problem is repairing a damaged human is a lot harder than simply scrapping a jet engine.

I see this all the time with those I work with, and occasionally within my own life. In the Syracuse area there is a mall that went through a major expansion. As mentioned earlier in the book, for whatever reason I cannot go into the new section. Vibration? Light frequency? Something else? I don't know. I can only make it a few minutes before needing to flee.

The first time I went into this new section I was in trouble. I ignored the growing uneasiness. Bad decision. Ten minutes in, it hit. I knew I needed to get out, and get out NOW! Despite the level of distress, and the desire to do so, I knew I could not crumble to the floor. Leaving in an ambulance was not something I was willing to do. I did what I needed to stay functional and got out.

It took me about five minutes to leave. And it took me about three days to recover from those five minutes. Many would say the experience was over when I got out. Some who understand may see it taking a little while to bounce back. I presume almost nobody would guess it could take three days to recover from a five-minute experience. The engine was pushed past 100%, damaged, and could not be thrown away. I did it because it was survival.

With kids I see this all the time. Someone is pushed too far, beyond the 100% mark. Just like with me in the mall, they know collapsing to the floor and/or falling apart will not end well for them. Sometimes they have no choice but to collapse or explode. Other times they hold it together, and to the casual observer they look fine. But they are not fine, and will not be fine. Damage is done.

I will illustrate with school because it is a common scenario, but this is by no means limited to a school setting. I had one kid I worked with pushed to the breaking point in class and asked to go to the bathroom to get out. He never came back. They eventually found him curled up in a corner crying. I have had multiple kids be dropped off at school and refuse to go in. Not just for a few minutes, but hours. It is not meltdown, or the typical kid not wanting to go to school stuff. These kids will say things like "I can't". If someone tries to get them out of the car they may flail or go limp. They may bite, throw, or spit in your face. It is a panic/survival response.

I have shown up at these situations and had kids only able to communicate with me through a stuffed animal. Others have been in a catatonic state, lost to the world. How damaged must a kid be to sit without activity or communication, motionless in a car for hours, rather than go into a school building? How bad must it be for them to irrationally lash out, knowing it will not end well for them, but equally feeling there is no other option?

These kids were pushed too far. Beyond 100%. Damage was done, and because it is the life of a child we obviously can't just throw away what is damaged. These kids will never be the same. They will return to being functional at some point, but damage is damage, and will be with them in some form forever. We don't get to throw away the engine. We have to try to fix what we have. In extreme cases I have seen some kids never able to return to a school building again.

If a person has to function beyond 100%, tapping emergency reserves that should only be used for survival, it comes at a huge cost. Pushing a jet engine past 100% is only done in life-threatening situations. The same should be true for our lives on the spectrum as well. We need to save survival-level reserves for survival-level situations.

The question is then how do we plan our day so that we don't get pushed too far and cause ourselves or someone else life-altering damage. There is an idea that we should give our day 100%. I disagree. Planning to give 100% is a bad idea. We need to plan for something to go wrong every day. We may not know what will go wrong, but it is almost guaranteed that something will go wrong. There is no such thing as a perfect day.

NASCAR race cars run at 100% when they race. The driver has that car engine maxed out, pushing the car so hard that there is a risk of crashing. Every piece of technology is at its limit trying to win the race. Knowing where that 100% line is, and pushing up to it but not past it, is great for winning a racing championship. It is a terrible way to live life. A little more than forty cars start each race. Several do not finish. When at that 100% threshold it only takes one minor mistake or misjudgment. It happens every race. Typically several will blow up an engine, get a flat tire, spin out into the wall, or face some other unexpected catastrophe. It is a part of racing. It shouldn't be a part of living life on the autism spectrum. I can't afford to constantly be crashing and tapping into survival-level reserves.

It is not unusual for the people I work with to routinely have such problems. They blow up their engine or crash daily. They are not at their core emotionally unstable people; the mistake they are making is that they make plans for their day to run at 100%, and leave nothing in reserve. It only takes one thing going wrong in any area of their life for them to be pushed too far, cross the 100% threshold, and trigger a crisis.

Every day something unexpected goes wrong. We have no way of knowing what problem to plan for, but it shouldn't matter. The plan can include readiness for unknown but expected daily problems. I know this doesn't make me sound very motivational. "Don't give every day your all." "Don't give it 100%." "Hold back a little." A more positive way to look at it would be like the Boy Scout motto of "Be prepared."

We put money in savings for when something bad happens. We don't know what or when, but we know it will happen at some point. When

I did winter camping I carried an emergency set of clothing and food. One time it saved my life because something went wrong.

Instead of 100% we should push ourselves only to 85% or 90%. This leaves something in reserve. It is not being lazy. It is being prepared. When our daily expected but unknown problem occurs it will suck up the 10 to 15% we kept in reserve for such problems. We don't crash, and are able to live life more successfully.

27. RELATIONSHIP PYRAMID

Part of what makes interpersonal interaction so difficult for someone on the autism spectrum is that the rules of interaction are incredibly complicated, and they change based on the type of relationship we have with the person. These rules change based on things such as: age, gender, official role, degree of closeness, history with the person, specifics unique to subculture and sub-subculture, physical location, and more. This is further complicated because these interpersonal rules are not written down anywhere, and are constantly changing as our culture changes.

To help people manage all these variables I have created a relationship pyramid to use as a tool. There any many different types of relationship pyramids for different purposes out there, and many can be found online. This specific relationship pyramid I created was for those on the autism spectrum to handle the ever-changing nuances of interpersonal relationships. Some aspects lie outside the central pyramid in the diagram, but it still works.

RELATIONSHIP PYRAMID

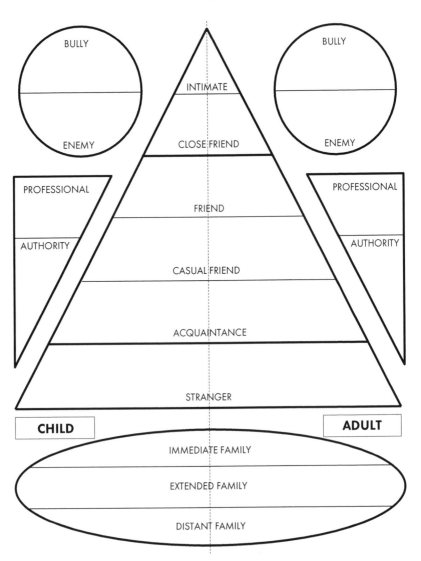

I encourage people to make multiple copies of the page with the relationship pyramid on it, enlarged to full page size, and write on it, using it to help sort out all the complexities and rules they encounter. I will explain the levels and categories, as well as how the tool can be used. Breaking things down into both adult and child there are twenty four different categories of relationships given. If this seems inadequate, certainly add your own. At the end of this chapter are suggestions of how to use the diagram. However, the uses are many, and there are certainly more than I have provided.

Stranger

Most relationship pyramids do not have a stranger section, but I discovered that for many with autism this section is essential. They don't really know what a stranger is. They need to know that a stranger is someone they have known for an extremely short period of time, and that what they know about them is only what the stranger has revealed. The information may not be accurate, and is certainly limited. There need to be rules about strangers for the purposes of safety, in areas such as: information shared, length of contact, requests made, location of contact, and so on.

Acquaintance

Acquaintance relationships are extremely short contacts over an extended period of time. They could be a frequent server, checkout clerk, neighbor, school janitor, and so on. There need to be rules here too, especially since acquaintance communication is small talk, and with autism we don't do small talk well. As a result we often over-share in this type of setting. There need to be rules about: types of conversations, length of conversations, requests, and so on.

A darker line is used between acquaintance and stranger on the diagram as acquaintance is the first level where there really is a relationship of any type, in the traditional sense.

Casual Friend

A casual friend is the first real friendship level. A casual friend is a friendship that centers around and does not cross beyond a singular shared location or activity. We might have a friend at school or work, but never do anything together outside those locations. Or maybe we know someone from karate class, but that is the limit of our interaction.

Rules for casual friends have to do with conversations not getting too deep, and not revealing overly personal information too quickly. It is the testing of the waters stage. Over time this relationship can grow, but it needs to be recognized for what it is right now. Many on the autism spectrum have trouble growing a relationship beyond this level.

Friend

The friend level differs from the casual friend in that activities tend to cross beyond singular locations and/or activities. We know and interact with this person in multiple settings. Enough time has passed, conversations have gotten deeper, and there is the real sharing of ideas and opinions. We are getting to the stage of sharing information which could be used against us if the other person chose to, but they do not. There is mutual enjoyment and seeking out of each other at this level, rather that one of running into each other at the mutual activity, or one-directional seeking, where one person is always doing the initiating of contact or communication.

Close Friend

A close friend is a relationship that has grown over a significant period of time (typically several years) and has gone through the other previous levels. Extensive sharing of information that could be used against each other is known at this level, and it is not used that way. These people will know most things about each other, and extended separation from the other person can be difficult.

There is a darker line between close friend and friend on the diagram because in the previous three levels people can be somewhat fluid with moving up and down over time. Once someone crosses into the close friend level they do not move back down the pyramid easily.

Intimate

Intimate does not necessarily mean a romantic or sexual relationship. It is an extremely close relationship that is a continuation and growth out of the close friend level. It takes extensive time to reach this level. There are no secrets, and one person truly completes and complements the other. Few reach this level, regardless of whether they are on the autism spectrum or not.

Immediate Family

Immediate family are those family members that we live with when growing up, and/or as adults those who we currently live with. Typically as a child this would include parents and siblings, but could include others as well who live within the home, such as grandparents. As adults it would potentially include our spouse and/or children.

Extended Family

Extended family members are those who do not live within the home, but who we have at least occasional regular contact with. The rules are different than for immediate family.

Distant Family

Distant family are people we may technically be related to, but rarely interact with in any way. We don't really know them, and they don't really know us. While technically family, the rules for this category would more closely align with that of a stranger or acquaintance than either of the other family levels.

Professional

Rules for professionals will vary based on the type and length of the professional relationship. A professional could be a teacher, therapist, doctor, coach, service provider, coworker, or anything similar.

Authority

There needs to be an understanding of the rules for people in authority such as: police officer, boss, school administrator, judge, and so on.

Bully

A bully is someone for whom we are a target of opportunity. They are who they are, and if we are not there they will be just as happy mistreating someone else. It is not personal.

Enemy

With an enemy the mistreatment is personal. They have a unique problem with us, and will seek us out to mistreat us.

Ideas on how to Use the Diagram

1. We can ask for help from a family member or mentor to place the people in our lives into the correct sections of the diagram. With autism we often misjudge relationships, and frequently place people we know at a higher level than they actually are. This creates problems because there are different rules for each of the different levels.

2. When studying and determining rules we can use this chapter and diagram to help us consider how the rules may change as the type, level, age, gender, and so on change within the relationships. Often changing any one of these variables results in a dramatic change within the rules.

3. We can write rules into each area of the diagram as we figure categories of them out, and if there's a blank section we know we have more work to do. The rules will change for each and every area on the chart, so if we can't figure out the differences between two or more areas we know we are missing something and should ask for help and/or do more research.

4. The diagram can serve as an aid and common frame of reference when we are working with professionals, such as therapists or mentors, helping us navigate culture and life with autism.

PART D

NOTES TO THE NON-AUTISTIC

28. LABELS

It is not unusual for me to encounter a parent concerned about "labeling" their kid with autism or anything else. There is a fear of creating disability where there is none, almost a self-fulfilling prophecy. There is also concern about prejudice and discrimination.

I want to offer a different perspective about labels. They can be useful. Imagine I have a picture of thirty two cans. A bit Andy Warhol, I know. Thirty one cans are labeled as chicken broth, and one has no label. Without knowing what is in the unlabeled can most people are going to make assumptions. The thirty one cans are chicken broth, and this unlabeled can is with the cans of broth. Outwardly it is the same size and shape. Most would assume the unlabeled can is chicken broth too. However, in this case, the unlabeled can is peaches.

I can take that can of peaches and put a broth label on it. However, that is just a thin piece of paper. It does not change what is in the can. Peaches are peaches, even if we want to pretend that it is a can of broth.

There's absolutely nothing wrong with a can of peaches. It is a very good thing. If I have thirty one cans of broth, and only one can of peaches, that makes the peaches something special, and even more valuable. I can do things with that one can of peaches that I cannot do with all those cans of broth.

However, I can't treat the can of peaches as if it is chicken broth. If I try to heat the contents of that can up, add vegetables and meat, what makes that can of peaches special will be lost and ruined.

Without having a label on that one can I have no idea what is inside. I have something useful and special, but I don't know it. It needs to be treated differently than all the other cans to reach its full potential. Putting a label on that can to identify it as peaches lets me know that I should treat it as peaches. That is a good thing.

People are clearly different than cans of either broth or peaches. However, as people we also identify ourselves with all sorts of labels. People routinely label themselves about everything from: gender, relationship status, religious, political, and/or philosophical beliefs; to things such as favorite movies, books, and employment history.

It is possible to make wrong assumptions about anyone based on a stereotypical idea of what a label means. Yet, we use these labels to identify ourselves anyway. It is a starting place for others to understand us.

When it comes to diagnostics, some people are worried by the idea of an autism spectrum diagnosis. But as an autistic person I did not dread the label. In fact it was exactly the opposite. Finally the whole world made sense. It allowed me to understand things about myself, and be successful in ways I could not before. I had been trying to function like a can of broth, and not doing too well. Recognizing I was instead a can of peaches made all the difference. Labels, like anything else, can be misunderstood or abused. However, labels can also be useful as a step toward greater success.

29. SELF-ADVOCACY STRUGGLES

Some parents and professionals advise that those on the autism spectrum need to learn to stand up and advocate for themselves. The concern is that it is a cruel world, and someone who cannot advocate effectively for themselves will not survive. This is a wonderful idea. Unfortunately it is not so simple.

Those on the autism spectrum are in need of some level of advocacy and assistance. I do not generally see autism as a disability, but in the area of self-advocacy the word disability may be appropriate. The ability to recognize a need for help and then seek the assistance of someone to advocate for them is what we should be aiming for.

The only people I have seen on the autism spectrum who have been capable of standing up for themselves in the moment are those who take a scorched earth approach to life and people. They come across as hostile, angry, and aggressive, and are not successful in life as a result. They may have successfully stood up for themselves in the moment, but not in a way that works. They lack many of the skills and attributes which allow someone to be successful in a more balanced way.

While an autistic person cannot self-advocate effectively, this is not to say they cannot be very effective and powerful advocates. There are many skilled attorneys and other advocates on the autism spectrum. However this advocacy is for others, avoiding the autism-based pitfalls of self-advocacy. These advocates live by the saying: "A person who represents themselves has a fool for a client and an attorney" (or advocate).

As we have discussed, with autism, we cannot think and feel at the same time. Connections in the brain will not allow it. If we are representing someone else we are in thinking mode, and nothing will stop us from getting the other person what they need. If we are representing ourselves, we are too close to the situation. Everything is emotion. We are useless.

To bridge the gap between the autism and non-autism worlds there needs to be a recognition that even the most capable and successful of those with autism are incapable of protecting themselves. There is a need for someone to stand up and protect them, or advocate on their behalf. Those on the spectrum typically make very loyal friends and workers, providing great benefits. Knowing they can be protected and safe will do a lot for them.

30. COMMITMENT AND CALCULATED RISK-TAKING

Some parents require their autistic kid, when committing to something, to follow through on that commitment to the very end. No quitting allowed. The goal may be to teach dedication. The result can be that the kid learns not to take risks in life.

It is important for an autistic kid to be able to explore options in their world. By being exposed to different things and trying new experiences, skills and abilities can surface, and they will have a more thorough understanding of people and culture. However, with autism there is often very little middle ground. We don't do something halfway. We either love something, or absolutely hate it.

If a kid can have freedom in how they explore different options, choose what they do or do not do, and decide how they engage in the world, they will be willing to take greater risks. They can try it. If it doesn't go well, or they don't like it, then they bail out. With this idea, they have nothing to lose. Take a risk and test the waters of a new experience.

By taking this risk they may find new skills and talents. They may connect with people. They may better understand a part of the world around them, or interpersonal relationships. It could trigger transitioning to a new special interest (perhaps away from video games and towards something more productive). It may be they find out what they hate, which is valuable too.

If a kid feels that by trying something new they will be trapped for a season, or however long the commitment is expected, it is much less likely they will be willing to take the risk. They will make sure any activity they are willing to do is completely "safe" and poses no challenge to them. Often this may mean an unwillingness to do much of anything or go anywhere (remember that video game obsession? I see a lot of it).

Yes, the kid begged and begged to sign up, and promised to do it forever. It is frustrating when they then want to drop it after a month and move on. They are exploring their world. They have no idea what they will or will not like without trying. As frustrating as exploring changing interests may be, we need to remember, there are autistic kids afraid to try anything. Even to leave the house.

I understand the desire and need to help our kids appreciate commitment. However, forcing a kid to stick with something is not the way to do it. That only teaches them to make safe decisions. We need them to be willing to take calculated risks.

What about commitment? For a person with autism to be really successful at something there needs to be passion. By feeling free to take risks, discovering and harnessing that idea of passion becomes much more likely. Think new special interest. When this passion is discovered commitment is no longer an issue. They will be driven to do whatever it is they are passionate about. They must do it because it is part of their very nature and being.

An autistic child who has found their passion will be begging to stay up late to work more on their project. You will be trying to pry them away from what they are doing to eat, or bathe, or making them promise to not get up in the middle of the night to do "X". There will be no begging (or threatening) them to get in the car to go someplace passion-oriented. They will be bugging you to hurry up so they are not late. When passion is harnessed nothing will be able to stop them and keep them from it. It is a part of their very being.

What should we do when they are ready to move on? We help them learn the appropriate way to end something. We do not talk to the person in charge. They do (with our help if needed). If they are being depended on for something coming up soon (a concert, game, art show, play, etc.) and there is no time for other arrangements, then they need to understand people are depending on them, and they can still quit, but need to take care of "X" first, because we don't hurt other people. It is the same way we give appropriate notice to an employer, even when quitting a job we hate.

Commitment is something important, and a concept that is fading. However, our autistic kids being willing to try new experiences without feeling like they might be trapped is more important. I want our kids to be willing to take calculated risks in life and not be afraid to choose any option that is not perfectly safe. Being willing to take risks may be what it takes for them to discover their passion, and take their life in a great new direction. I'm also not aware of many successful people in life, especially with autism, who are unwilling to take calculated risks, and/or experience failure.

31. AGE APPROPRIATE

There is an innocence and naivety that goes with autism. Interests can be younger than considered typical. Some in the autism world are concerned that our kids on the spectrum should be age appropriate. They try to eliminate what is not age appropriate in the child. The goal? Trying to avoid bullying by getting rid of what could make the child a target, as well as helping them fit in socially. How I wish it was that simple.

Living life in this world is difficult with autism. Having younger than typical interests can be comfortable and safe. It's like emotional comfort food. There is a sense of relief. This is what leisure and entertainment should be about. Real life is already difficult enough.

If we are taking something "too young" away, what will it be replaced by? We have created a vacuum. What the world considers age appropriate can be pretty scary. Our kids are typically innocent and a little behind their peers. They may not be ready. Harm can be done. This is one of those autism areas where different can be better: I'd gladly take innocent and naive over the alternatives.

I was recently in a school meeting on behalf of a ten-year-old boy on the spectrum who I was working with. The school social worker was concerned that he had begun to bring toys to school. She said fifth grade boys do not bring toys to school, and that it needed to stop. But I knew exactly which toys this boy was bringing to school. I had given them to him.

The family made it clear that he would continue to bring the toys, and why. Things that are not "age appropriate" can serve an important function. These toys were connected to this boy's autistic special interest, and played a role in his emotional stability. They were a part of his success.

I understand wanting to protect our kids from bullies. Looking and acting like everyone else can make this easier, and there is a time and a place for this. Unfortunately our autistic kids are a target-rich environment. There is plenty to be picked on about, and taking away items that are not considered "age appropriate" will not solve the problem of bullies. I know this is not fair, but all too often it is the reality.

How do we make decisions about age appropriateness for our kids? We don't. It is their decision. We educate, support, and get out of the way.

We have a responsibility to teach our autistic kids about non-autism culture. This encompasses a lot, including what is considered age appropriate, and what is not. With autism, cultural knowledge and skills will not be picked up through just living life. They need to be intellectually taught. It is the same as teaching them anything else in life. What we do not do is make the decision for them. After educating them, we get out of the way. The decision about what to do is now theirs to make.

Several years ago I gave a few clip-on stuffed animals to an autistic eleven-year-old boy. He loved them. He immediately clipped them to his school bag. I knew that would make him a greater target. I asked him how many other boys at school had clip-on stuffed animals on their school bags. He replied none of them did. I explained he may get picked on by other kids for having them on his bag, and why, but if he wanted the stuffed animals on his bag there was nothing wrong with it. I told him it was his decision. He said he liked them, and as long as there was nothing wrong with it he wanted them on his school bag, and didn't care about what the other kids would say.

I gave him the cultural education he needed for this situation. He knew he had my support no matter what he decided. The decision about what to do was then his. I gave the education, options, unconditional acceptance, and freedom to choose. The family did too.

There is a benefit to knowing how to fit in; sometimes it can be important, even critical. Culture needs to be taught to keep our kids safe and successful. However, when it comes to interests, as long as there is nothing wrong with it, it is then their decision to make. If it causes them problems we can remind and re-educate. We help them weigh the costs and benefits, but don't decide for them. It still remains their decision.

This boy never changed his mind, and the stuffed animals remained on his school bag. I admire this kid. He knew who he was and what he wanted. Yes he was picked on by a few kids for the stuffed animals. But he was picked on for other things at school too. He was smart enough to recognize that conforming to what some thought "age appropriate" would not solve his bully problem. He did the cost benefit analysis and decided the stuffed animals stayed.

32. DISCIPLINE

One of the most commonly asked questions I hear from parents is how to discipline their autistic child. They have tried all the common and advised techniques with absolutely none of them working.

Punishment does not work with autism. It doesn't. As parents we need to get over our control issues. As much as we might want punishment to work, it will not work with autism. It is like kicking a puppy. The one doing the kicking might feel better, but the puppy is traumatized and nothing has been learned. This does not mean there are not discipline solutions.

When I say discipline I do not mean punishment. I presume the real goal of parents is not to punish their kids. That would be sadistic. The real goal is modifying or molding behavior for success. That is what I am writing about with discipline. It is how we successfully change behavior.

Conventional wisdom (and many books) says discipline needs to be handled immediately for it to be effective. That is not how it works with autism. With autism discipline cannot be handled immediately.

It will not work, and will only make things worse.

There are three stages to discipline with autism. There are hours or even days between them, and all three stages are not always possible or appropriate.

Stage 1: This is handling things in the moment to make sure everything is okay and everyone is safe. It is the immediate fixing and stabilizing. I suggest reading chapter fifteen on the brain switch for techniques that are autism-based on how to do this.

Stage 2: This is finding out what happened. This will happen hours or days later than Stage 1. Even if we saw it happen and think we know the whole story we need to find out from them what happened. We don't know what they were thinking or feeling. We don't know what else may have happened that influences this situation. We don't know motivation. Remember, with autism it is not unusual for bad things to happen despite good intentions.

As adults we are tempted to add commentary, or pose statements in the form of questions. We can also be pretty judgmental. None of that can happen here in Stage 2. We need to let our egos go. All we care about is what happened. This is a short conversation, and ideally one-sided. The kid shows up and talks for fifteen seconds to maybe a minute or so. If we say anything it needs to be nothing more than a legitimate question to get better understanding. Also, there's no need for eye contact. Autism, remember.

I have seen when kids are used to this process that they will decide on their own when this happens, or if it happens at all. There are times they will not talk, and that is okay. I have seen that when the kid picks the time it will usually be when the parent is in the middle of something and does not want to be disturbed. That way everyone wants to keep it short and avoid eye contact. Our kids are autistic. Not stupid.

Stage 3: This stage comes typically days later rather than hours later, if it comes at all. The goal of Stage 3 is to prevent certain issues arising again in the future. We want to change behavior. However, there are strict criteria that need to be met before we go ahead with Stage 3.

First, it needs to be an issue that will matter a year from now. There are so many things in the lives of our kids that will matter a year from now that we can't spend time and energy on something that will not. It would be counterproductive. I know we have ways of convincing ourselves almost anything will matter a year from now. But we must be honest with ourselves. Will this really matter?

The second requirement is that the issue must be a pattern. Even if it is something considered a huge problem (suspended from school, trouble with the law, etc.), if it has never happened before, and there is no indication it will happen again, we should not bring it up. People do stupid things, including people on the autism spectrum. Let it go. We are looking for patterns of problems.

Once we have established a pattern of something problematic that will matter a year from now, we can begin Stage 3.

In Stage 3 the approach we take is to emphasize that we recognize a problem, and suggest that we work together with the child to solve it. There are important rules to bear in mind with this stage: first, everything must be present tense or future tense. We should never go back into the past. With autism there is often a phenomenal long-term memory, and they are not stupid. The autistic kid will know what the conversation is about. So no need to rub their nose in it. If we do, we are done, and it will end badly. Show them the courtesy of not bringing up specific events, so they can maintain their dignity and respect. This is not about winning. It is about changed behavior.

In Stage 3 we also keep things focused on the positive, and give the kid every benefit of the doubt on their motivation. We focus on helping them be more successful and solve problems. With autism things go bad, a lot. However, motives and goals with autism typically are good. Much more so than with the general population.

So how do we keep to using the present/future tense while remaining positive? Here's an example of what not to say: "Remember when we were grocery shopping and we had that horrible meltdown, and I had to leave the cart there and drag you screaming to the car? We can't have that again in the future." (I have actually seen this done by parents.) What we should say instead is something like: "I know grocery shopping is hard for you, but sometimes we need to take you with us. Let's work together and find ways to help make it easier for you to be successful." This second statement is set in the present/future, allows the kid to save face, and is done without judgement focusing on solving problems. It will work.

There are times when moral situations may crop up. Though this may be harder, I would treat it the same way. For example: "You have a habit of taking things that are not yours. Let's work together to help you find ways to only take things which belong to you." Obviously in that type of situation a lot of work would need to go into unravelling why the kid is doing what they are doing. That is partly why Stage 2, if handled correctly, can be so valuable. We get the information we need because the child feels safe in talking and giving us their inner thoughts and motivations.

Battles

With the issue of discipline and parenting, common sense needs to come into play too. As we saw earlier in chapter two, parents we need to win all battles. All of them. However, we do not always need to fight the battle at all. I mastered the art of seeing a battle coming and stepping aside to let it go by. If the battle began then I had to fight it until it was won, and sometimes in the end it just wasn't worth it. Life with our kids should not be a power struggle, with us as adults asserting our superiority. It is about raising responsible children and preparing them to be responsible adults. Similarly, if I know my kid is having a bad day, I'm smart enough to not make an issue out of the empty bottle left on the counter. It can wait for another day. This might be allowing my kid to be less than perfect, but then I too am less than perfect.

One thing that always helped me was asking myself: "If an adult had done the same thing, how would I respond?" Would what I saw as horrible and unreasonable with a kid all of a sudden be okay? If so, I needed to change my attitude. It was also true that the things which bugged me the most were also the areas of my own personal weakness. For example, I might catch myself about to say something to the kid for the mess left in the kitchen, and then realize I was the one who left the mess. Moments like these helped give me perspective.

Natural Consequences

While we do not punish, and we use the three-stage discipline process, we also do not protect them from natural consequences. Natural consequences work. I know a lot of people who create a punishment and call it a consequence. This is not a natural consequence. I am talking a true natural outgrowth of the action.

I once worked with an autistic kid who had the habit of running his mouth. He would tell everyone exactly what he thought, why everyone else was inferior, how he was always right, and everyone else wrong. Mix in a bit of snarky attitude too. This had been picked up on and addressed by parents, teachers, mentors, and myself. Finally, one day in the school hallway he ran his mouth to the wrong person at the wrong time. He turned to continue walking, and the person that he ran his mouth to came up behind him and beat him to a pulp. Teachers intervened, but a lot can happen in just a few seconds.

Parents did the right thing and lovingly took their child for medical treatment with him crying on their shoulder. Not one person ever said anything about him running his mouth. However, he learned his lesson and never did it again. The natural consequences of running your mouth are that you may get beat up in the hallway. All the adults involved, while wishing the experience had never happened, and feeling for the boy who got beat up, were also glad of the lesson learned. Better to learn about running your mouth at eleven years old in a school hallway than in your twenties or thirties in a bar fight.

Unfortunately I see parents who are willing to punish their kids, but protect them from natural consequences. These are kids who never feel at fault for anything in their lives, who grow into adults unable to function in the real world. This is not disability due to autism. This is disability created by poor parenting. Avoiding natural consequences means escaping responsibility. And part of natural consequences is that we fix what we broke. It is owning the situation, even if we don't want to. It is focusing on changing behavior and preparing for adult life.

We can get creative with this. I know someone with an autistic kid who left empty yogurt cups and grape stems all over the place. The parents don't punish, but the kid needs to own the issue: bed filled with yogurt cups and grape stems. Another parent had a kid who left puddles of water all over the floor. Kid gets woken up in the middle of the night to dry the puddles. Didn't do dishes last night like they were supposed to? Get woken up an hour early the next morning to do the dishes. None of this is punishment. We have not created an artificial situation. No one was grounded. No one lost use of their electronics. There were no lost privileges or extra chores of any kind. It is simply holding someone accountable. They must own the situation and make it right.

Societal Authority

While unpleasant to think about, there are times natural consequences involve authorities such as school officials or law enforcement. The natural consequences of living in a civilized society involve agreed-upon laws and standards for all. While sometimes unpleasant, if an autistic person is to live and function in society, they need to live by the same rules as everyone else in that society. If they are incapable of this they are destined to spend the rest of their life in an institution. It may be an institution for the disabled, or it may be prison. Yes, prisons are full of autistic individuals who couldn't or wouldn't live by the same rules as everyone else.

There are times societal authority can be softened, and times it should not. If a kid gets in trouble because they lack interpersonal skills and said or did something rude or inappropriate, that is a result of the autism and what we would call impaired theory of mind. It is the inability on an instinctive level to understand emotions, intent, or what is culturally or socially appropriate. When we are dealing with a crime or offence of intent, such as insubordination or harassment, especially with a younger individual, it may (but not always) be appropriate to put the situation into context for the person in authority. This issue is coming from a place of disability, as a part of the diagnosis, and has not happened before. It is still a problem, it may be a major problem, and if the person is to live in society it must be addressed.

Note that I said in the paragraph above that impaired theory of mind only applies to instinct. It does not mean that the same information cannot be intellectually learned. The first time a kid ignores what a person in authority tells them to do, assuming this is a reasonable request, it could be impaired theory of mind. They are still responsible for the behavior and need to make it right, and may suffer milder but appropriate societal consequences. Over time, however, presuming the child is told that they must follow the reasonable requests and commands of a legitimate authority figure, impaired theory of mind is no longer in play. They should be able to intellectually know that they should follow the directive, and can raise their objections later. They may not like that they must follow authority, and believe that the authority figure is wrong (and they may be), but they do what they are told and do not argue their case at that time.

Therefore, if the child continues to ignore authority, the societal consequences will be worse. They no longer have the excuse that they didn't know ignoring reasonable requests and orders from a legitimate authority was inappropriate behavior. Where does it end? Either the individual learns to follow appropriate authority, or they may end up tazed, shot, and/or under arrest. Following authority is only one example. There are many standards and rules we must follow to live in society, that none of us are exempt from, even the autistic. If someone is incapable or unwilling, then they cannot live and function in society and other arrangements must be made.

33. PHILOSOPHY OF CARE

My approach to helping those on the autism spectrum who are having a difficult time is very similar to the approach taken when someone breaks their arm. The solution is knowing what to do, and when to do it.

When someone breaks their arm we put a cast on, creating an artificial environment catered to what their needs are. That cast is designed to hold things in place, create stability, and allow healing. Then during that healing process different therapies are used to strengthen the arm, even while the cast remains on. It is preparing the arm for when that protective artificial environment is removed. We know the cast must eventually come off, else it causes atrophy, hinders growth, and the arm is useless: it no longer has the strength to adequately function. However, we also know that if the cast comes off too soon, or is never put on to begin with, we can create further injury. The arm doesn't heal right, and is a mess for good. The solution is knowing what to do (put on a cast and have physical therapy), and when to do it (when to put on the cast and when to remove it).

The same is true for helping an autistic child who is struggling to function. This ties in with chapter one about petting the cat, and why those of us on the autism spectrum have some of the difficulties we do. For helping someone be successful with autism there can be two competing goals and agendas. One is to stabilize and heal. The other is to prepare for the "real world". There is a time for each.

There are times parents lean too heavily towards preparing their child for the "real world". These people know the pressures and burdens of life in society, and they want the child to be successful. I help these people understand that while the child will eventually need to live in the real world like the rest of us, at the moment the child is in need of healing and strengthening. That stability is the foundation for developing everything else that the child will need in the real world. Without that stable foundation, nothing else will be accomplished. For these kids we start by creating an artificial world, catered to them and their needs. This world we are creating is a little bubble that does not reflect reality, but just like the cast on the broken arm, will allow time for healing and strengthening.

Having said that, to not prepare and equip the child for reality is doing them a disservice. At some point the "cast" has to gently come off. Protect too much and/or too long and we create disability. That person may indeed not be able to function in society. How long does the "cast" stay on? It is different from person to person, situation to situation.

Before the "cast" comes off we need to have healing that is strong and stable. We also need an understanding of the strengths and weaknesses of autism. We should also have put in place autism-based skills to equip that person to be successful in the realities of the world. It is then a process over time of gently removing the cast, trying out the new learned abilities with practice and support. It is knowing what to do, how and when to do it, moving along the path for success.

Just to be clear, the real world with autism will still look different than the real world for most people. My life as an autistic adult is different than the life of most adults. That is not a bad thing. I like my life, and would have it no other way, but it has its differences. We are not eliminating autism, but equipping autistic people to be successful in a world not set up for autism.

A lot of parents have a hard time striking this balance with their kids. They are too close to the situation, and the line between what is too much and not enough is constantly moving. This is part of the benefit of working with a skilled professional. They can help as a sounding board for making these judgement calls.

However, don't follow anyone blindly. Even me. I tell families I work with that we are a team. While I am an expert in autism, they are an expert in their kid. I could work with their child the rest of my life and not know the child the way they do. If the parents and I disagree, I need to figure out why. Am I not explaining something clearly enough? Is there information I'm lacking about the kid that the family has? I encourage everyone I work with to doubt and question me. We have to get it right. We are responsible for someone's life.

The path to success is a skilled balancing act of knowing what to do and when to do it. Lean too much one way we cause damage. Too much the other way we create disability.

34. ACADEMICS

This is not a book on the education system and autism. As such there are far too many differences and nuances in providing a formal education to a person on the autism spectrum than can be properly explored here. However, a few deserve attention.

I will admit I come at the issue of education with some biases based on my life experience. While I have always loved knowledge and learning, I did not do well in school. I have hanging on the wall in my office framed samples of my school progress reports and report cards. One of them indicates my mid-term average in the class was 5 out of 120. Others talk about my not working up to my abilities, showing up unprepared, or having an attitude of not caring. I have so many of these notes it was difficult to decide what to frame and hang.

As we saw in the "My Life" introduction to this book, I was never supposed to make it, and I almost didn't. My severe dysgraphia most likely contributed heavily to not doing well. Even as an adult I have trouble doing much more than signing my own name, and my handwriting is all but illegible in all capital letters. Spelling tests were a nightmare, even after studying hard. Remember, I love knowledge and learning. That is different to formal education. Those vying for class valedictorian would want to be my lab partner. I could explain it all to them so it made sense, helping them excel, but I was unable to communicate the information in a lab report of my own. They got an "A". I got a zero. I would discuss the finer points of Shakespeare or Chaucer, but was incapable of writing and handing in the paper. For me a lot of the formal school work failed my cost benefit analysis, and I just didn't do it.

I am successful in spite of my education. Not because of it. As a kid I focused my life on other priorities. Studying and understanding people. Teaching. Public speaking. Serving others. Thinking about life priorities and goals. If I had it to do over again I would do the same thing.

Educational Priorities

I have seen many cases where a focus on education has been a path to failure for those on the autism spectrum. It has not been unusual for me to find a person on the autism spectrum who did well in school, including college-educated, but who can't get or keep a job as simple as stocking shelves. They may be academically educated, but lack everything else required to function in life.

Formal education can be a misplaced priority. We want a successful life. We shouldn't be confusing education with success. Education can be part of a path to success, but education is not a singular path to success, nor do I think it is one of the most important factors. I have for example worked with an eight-year-old doing college-level physics. Clearly education will play a role in success for this person; however even with this giftedness, he needs other autism-based strategies for a successful life. Education and knowledge are not enough. Fortunately the family understands that. Not all do.

I have had parents tell me they could not hold their kids accountable for anything non-schoolwork related in their life because their grades might suffer. I have had parents tell me their kids could not focus on developing other autism-based success skills because they needed to focus on education. I have had parents go to college class with their kids, take the notes themselves, spoon feed them through the papers and projects, and/or argue that grade schools should not hold their kids accountable for their actions. These kids may graduate and get a degree, but are unprepared to live life. These are extreme examples, but not uncommon either.

Education can be a good thing. However, with autism formal academic education is not a standalone key to success. I work with a lot of adults. Not once have I had an adult lose a job or have work performance issues because of a lack of ability to do the technical aspects of the job. I have had many who have lost jobs or experienced other work difficulties because of all the other autism-related challenges. If you are depending solely on education to bring you success in the world, it will not happen.

Success requires effort in areas that matter from an autism perspective. It is the things in life most people take for granted that we with autism struggle with. Study culture. Study people. Learn and master autism-based skills. When I was a kid those were the decisions I made. I knew I could not do it all. I focused on the people skills. Would it be nice to have had better grades? Certainly. Would it have been nice to not have parents and teachers on my case all the time about not doing homework or not performing up to my abilities? Absolutely! But if I had it to do over again would I have done it differently? No I would not!

I think it is true that if I was a kid in today's age I would have had more academic success. In the 1970s and 80s there were no such things as individualized education plans or academic supports. There were no computers allowing differing options about how to accomplish tasks. Yes, for a couple years I was in a self-contained room that had an aide, and while I had some horrible teachers who didn't understand me or my struggles, I had some good ones too. I grew up in a different world. Either you could do it or you couldn't. I have no regrets about the decisions I made at that time.

While there are things more important than formal education, there are also autism-based strategies which can help a person on the autism spectrum be more successful in school. Formal education is not a bad thing. It is just not one of the most important thing for success. I have fully supported people on the autism spectrum who have done well in the area of formal education, but who are also able to keep priorities and life in balance.

Homework

Homework is counterproductive for kids on the autism spectrum. It does not match the way an autistic student learns and processes information. It can also be damaging, as explored below. I recommend its elimination. Once understood, many schools go along with eliminating homework. As a professional I typically get more pushback from parents than from schools.

If there is a longer term project I can support that for autistic students. There may still need to be accommodations made, and supports put in place, but in this case it is real learning that reflects and patterns life. That is not what I am talking about with homework. What I have a problem with is the routine repetitive homework that accounts for the bulk of what is assigned.

With autism learning comes in significant jumps, not the gradual progression that most non-autistic people experience. We learn something when we have intellectual mastery of the idea. Until then we are totally clueless. There isn't much between these two states for those of us on the spectrum.

If an autistic person has total mastery of an idea, proving that mastery over and over again on paper is just wasting their time. Autistic people hate to have their time wasted. It is illogical. If something is illogical to us we just can't do it, regardless of the outcome. It will not happen. I'm not saying that is right. Only that it's the way it is.

If the autistic student hasn't mastered the idea yet, then they will be totally clueless about how to complete what is being asked in the homework. With autism we are already perfectionistic, have high anxiety, and typically a low self-image. Demonstrating that we are clueless about a topic over and over again presents a problem. If there isn't a constant battle and meltdown, there can still be internal damage.

As you will recall, with autism we are incapable of thinking and feeling at the same time. If we are upset because we have mastered a topic and our time is being wasted, we are feeling, not thinking. If we are upset because we are clueless about how to do the assignment, we are feeling, not thinking. Assuming the purpose of homework is to learn, that learning requires the use of the fact based frontal lobe so we can think. The thought processes needed to learn are impossible because the autistic person is stuck in feeling mode. They can't think and feel at the same time. Learning does not happen.

Given the pennies in the cup theory (emotional energy), it is important to carefully consider priorities. With autism we are not only having to learn the academics intellectually, but everything else in life too, that most people take for granted. We need instruction and help in areas such as communication, relationships, body language, facial expressions, social rules, flexibility, sensory regulation, and culture. Are those math problems or vocabulary questions really that important when compared to this list? For those who say they need to learn the academics to survive in life, I will say that they need to learn the other skills too, and the other skills are likely much more important and much harder to learn. We can only spend a penny from the cup once. Do so wisely.

Then there is the issue of compartmentalization. What happens at school stays at school. This makes sense because so many kids come home from school overwhelmed. All day they are not only trying to learn the academics, but all the other autism-based skills as well. The autistic student needs to try to figure everything out intellectually, and typically no one explains things in a way that makes sense to them. After school they are intellectually, emotionally, and physically done. When getting home it is not unusual for an autistic kid to isolate themselves from others for a while, immerse themselves in their special interest, or sleep.

Some typical students do benefit from the repetition and practice that homework provides. This is not true with autism. We have executive functioning and processing struggles. The more we do something, especially in quick succession, the worse we can get. The first time we do it will be the easiest. The second time harder. The third and subsequent times even worse. With autism almost everything we do is processed at the conscious intellectual level. It is a lot of work, and a hard way to live life. We get tired and worn out. Everything can become backed up and not processed appropriately.

It is like when at a major event not equipped for large crowds everyone goes to leave at once. The first few people and their cars may get through with little trouble. After that it is a mess. The small exit combined with the narrow road makes for a hopeless traffic jam. Accidents, enraged tempers, pushy drivers, and driving on the shoulder are all common.

When we have the brain equivalent of accidents, pushy drivers, and so on from our mental traffic jam, processing suffers. Not only can it take a while for things to clear, the data can be corrupted, and the confusion grows. I can eventually get an elephant through a soda straw; however, when I am done it may not look much like an elephant anymore, and it will take me a really long time to do it.

This information corruption potential is made worse by the autistic mental filing system. Information in the brain is "tagged" based on content, relevance, and cross application. When the information is learned, assuming proper tagging and filing, it is there for retrieval as needed. As we are "relearning" this information with homework, resulting in the mental traffic jam, and functioning on the emotional level, we can damage the tagging that was done when the information was originally learned, and then impair the ability to retrieve the information when it is really needed. It would be as if I took my neatly filed drawer of information out of my desk and threw the files all over the room. All the information might technically still be there, but good luck finding it.

I know parents are concerned that their kids be successful. We do not want to raise them to be handicapped. For many parents homework is one of those concerns. As parents we sometimes need to fight hard battles with our kids. But this is not one of those times. Eliminating homework will not hinder your autistic child's learning. They will learn better. Eliminating homework will neither keep your child out of a good college, nor keep them from getting a good job. This success will be based on who they are, and what they know, not on having done or not done homework.

Look at the big picture when it comes to success. Eliminating homework will allow your autistic child better emotional health and balance. Eliminating homework can allow your autistic child to learn better. Eliminating homework will allow you and them additional time and energy to focus on the full range of what they need to learn to be successful in life with autism. Eliminating homework can also improve your relationship with your child as it is often a damaging point of conflict. These themes of success and empowerment are what will really make a difference in the life of your child.

I recognize that advising parents that homework is counterproductive and damaging to autistic students is only half the equation. The school is the other half, and they must also be on board.

Education Philosophy

One of the huge challenges in formal education is that with autism we are at our core different than most formal educators. With autism we are goal-oriented. Educators and modern formal education tend to be process-oriented. First you do "A", then you do "B", and if you follow all the steps correctly you will get the right answer. With autism, we want the best, fastest, most efficient way to get the answer. Our goal is solving the problem, not jumping through process-oriented hoops. It is a completely different approach to life.

I have had process-oriented educators say that unless a student learns to follow all the steps of a process they will be unable to solve the problem when the work becomes harder. With autism that is not necessarily true. The teacher or someone else may not be able to solve more complex problems differently, but the autistic student often can. I have seen students on the autism spectrum capable of absolutely amazing things when it comes to creative problem-solving. It may be different, but it works.

With autism we learn differently, and process information differently. I believe that should allow us different freedoms in the area of education. The goal should be can we do it, not that we do it exactly the same way someone else does it.

One of the biggest areas this comes up is in the area of showing or explaining work. My own biased personal opinion, which I cannot officially support in my work, is that if the student gets the right answer then no one should care if they show their work or not. However, in the adult world simply being right isn't always enough. Often we have to be able to prove it on paper. What I can officially support is that if a student solves a problem in a different way than the teacher expected or taught, but can show how they came to their conclusions or answer, that different process should be honored, and I will fight to have it honored. People who change the world don't blindly follow how everyone else does things.

Type of Teacher

When I think of people who go into teaching as a profession they are typically very different to their autistic students. We already identified process- verses goal-oriented, but there is more. They typically loved school. They felt loved, supported, and fulfilled in an education environment. They joined clubs. They went to dances. They were involved in athletics. They had lots of friends and even romantic relationships. They did well in school. None of this makes them a bad teacher or a bad person. What it does mean is that it can be harder for them to understand the pitfalls, frustrations, and problems that our kids go through on a daily basis. They may still be the right person to teach our kid, but it can pose a challenge to overcome.

There are a handful of people who entered the field of education for a different reason. They hated school, and did horribly. They didn't have friends, were picked on, and rather than participate in extracurricular activities they wanted to get out of the building as soon as they could, and never go back. Going to prom was never a part of their plans. They failed courses, and have been fired from jobs. Like our kids, they have had to fight and struggle for everything they have. This is no assurance that they are a good teacher or a good person, and they may be wrong for our child, but I wish more people in formal education had some experiences like this, so that they could know what it is like to walk a mile in our kids' shoes.

Relationship-Based

One huge factor I tell both kids and educators is that it is important to get to know each other as people. Things such as: hobbies, family, personalities, and creating a mutual understanding and appreciation of each other. It is critical for a child on the autism spectrum to like their teacher and to think their teacher likes them: they will be willing to work harder, and it also buys them the benefit of the doubt in grey areas. They will perform at their best. If the child doesn't like their teacher, or thinks the teacher doesn't like them, even in an area of strength, they will not do well in the course, and stand a good chance of failing. Being black and white about many things in life is a part of autism, and it extends to people. This is also true for adults on the spectrum. If we do not like our boss we had better start looking for a new job because our days will be numbered.

Typical Accommodations and Supports

These are the standard accommodations and supports that I put into the plan for most kids I work with. I'll try to explain briefly the rationale behind each below.

- Ability to walk out of any class, at any time, for any reason, and go to a pre-approved safe location. The amount of time they can spend there is unlimited, and they do not need to talk with or process anything with anyone. They are responsible for the information covered in that class, and that information will need to be made up another time such as after school, or in another way, such as reading or interacting with another student, or potentially accepting a lower grade due to not knowing information or having missing work.

  - If we do not allow a kid a safe exit they can be damaged. Remember the student who was overwhelmed and the only way to get out was to go to the bathroom? He never came back. They eventually found him curled up in a corner sobbing. This should never have to happen to a child.

  - Schools will often want to put a limit on the amount of time spent out of class before the student needs to return. This does not work because there are too many variables that influence how much time a kid needs. I have seen it be legitimately anywhere from a few minutes to all day. The student is accountable for the information missed. They are not getting out of anything. It is managing life.

  - A student may not be capable in the moment of asking for permission, informing the teacher where they are going, or getting a pass. Such communication may be beyond where they are at in the moment.

- A student should be provided a copy of class notes, and not be asked to take notes in any way. Notes can be a copy of the teacher's, or obtained from another student anonymously by the teacher on behalf of the autistic student. Any "fill in the blank" worksheets to be done during the class lecture are to be provided already filled in.

  o With autism we can't multi-task. Walking and chewing gum at the same time counts as multi-tasking. If someone is taking notes they are not able to adequately process and mentally file the information for later recall.

  o With autism we are goal-oriented, not process-oriented. If taking notes, the goal becomes to take notes, not learn. If filling in a worksheet, the goal is filling in the right word, not learning.

  o Dysgraphia, dyslexia, dyscalculia and more are all common learning disabilities with autism, and they often go undiagnosed. While they are not always present, they are commonly a factor that impact things such as note-taking for the students with these issues.

- No homework, or at a minimum significantly modified homework – not for content, but for length.

  o Reasoning dealt with in the previous homework section of this chapter.

- Ability to, if they choose, eat lunch in a different quieter and/or more private location than the lunch room. Also, if they choose, they can bring a friend or two with them for socialization.

  o Sensory management.

  o Interpersonal safety with getting picked on and similar.

- The ability to leave class a few minutes early when changing classes.
  - o Avoids sensory problems in the hallway.
  - o Offers protection from bullies and other social problems because the autistic student will mostly be alone in the hallway.
- Some method for sensory management within the classroom, specific to the sensory needs of the student.
  - o If a student has sensory needs this will interfere with learning and heighten anxiety, which also interferes with learning.
  - o Occupational therapy a few times a week will not manage the sensory needs of a student. It is an all-day every-day thing.
- Consider preferred seating.
  - o Potential for sensory distractions.
  - o Potential for problems with other students that they are best kept away from.
- If the student qualifies for an aide, awareness that the aide may be needed more in the less-structured times of the day, such as hallways, recess, lunch room, specials, and so on. It is not just the academic classroom need. If the child does not qualify for an aide, at least arrange for someone to keep an eye on the student and make sure things are going okay.
  - o Less structure means significantly more social and interpersonal complexity, playing to the weaknesses of the person on the autism spectrum.
  - o Less structure means more interpersonal vulnerability to bullies and other similar problems.

Negotiating Tip

There are times we have to go to war with the school district to get a kid what they need. It should not be the first step, but I have been there. As a parent I was on the phone hiring an attorney when I received the call from the district on the other line agreeing to place my kid in the program he needed. I have been in a meeting as a professional when I had a teacher in tears asking why I was so mean and hated everyone, while the chair of the meeting was calling the district home office to figure out what to do. I know how to play hard ball, and get the students I am representing what they need.

However, I rarely use this type of tough approach, and only resort to difficult tactics when all else has failed. It should never be a way of life. I would much rather collaborate with a team approach, working towards solutions. I allow if at all possible every opportunity for someone else to save face, or adopt my ideas and goals as their own. I am not there to do battle and win. I am there to get the child what they need.

Some people do battle with the school district as a way of life. The district is the enemy and they are to be defeated. This is counter-productive in many ways. There are times I have badgered a district into giving me what I need for a student. I have made it easier to give me what I want than to get rid of me. I got what the kid needed not because the district necessarily believed in what I was saying, but because it was easier than fighting me. At this point of concession I would again be grateful, cooperative, and an easy person to deal with. If someone has the attitude of perpetual war with a school district, the district will conclude that no matter what they do they will not win, and that you will continue to make their life miserable. Once the district concludes there is no way they can win, and it will be a never-ending battle, they will concede that their life will be miserable, but they will also conclude that as long as they are miserable you will be too, and there will never be another concession from the district that they do not completely believe in.

When I negotiate with a district I prioritize my issues into three categories.

1. What I absolutely must have.
2. What it is really important to have.
3. What would be good to have, but I can live without.

I accept I may not be able to get everything, and that life is not perfect. I want to prioritize my needs for each student going into the meeting based upon what is most critical for their success.

Also, a great written plan is not everything. I would much rather have a teacher or school that really cares about a kid and wants to help them without any formal plan in place, than a teacher or school with a perfect written plan, but the goal is to follow the written plan and not focus on the needs of the student.

Going into a meeting, unless it is routine, I recommend that as a parent you take someone with you to function as an advocate. Even if you are an excellent advocate, having someone else there allows you to be in that meeting as a parent rather than as an advocate, which is a completely different role. While I have shared some of these observations on advocacy, this hasn't really been a "how to advocate" section as much as it has been about what to watch out for in an advocacy setting.

35. WHO DOES WELL IN LIFE

I am often asked by parents how I think their kid will do in life, and if there is anything that can be done to improve the odds of success. Parents want hope, as well as an accurate assessment of what the future may hold. Will their child live independently? Will their child be capable of having a family? Will their child have a job? Will their child generally be a happy functional member of society?

Often, especially with a younger kid, I have to tell the family that I have no idea what the future may hold, but that I have hope and routinely see amazing things that most would consider impossible. I also tell them that there are nine factors that are indicative of, or contribute towards, a successful life with autism. Of the nine, only two are beyond someone's control.

Higher IQ
Obviously IQ is not something in our control, but it does make a difference in how successful a person can be in life with autism. The

reason is that a lot of the techniques involved in being successful with autism require mental power and capacity. To be successful with autism requires holding the natural instinctive response in check, and then replacing that response with one intellectually determined and executed. That requires average or higher brain power.

Be aware, this is only one of nine factors indicative of or contributing toward success with autism. I know people who have unmeasurably low IQs, who – though they may never live independently – in most respects live a wonderfully successful life. IQ is part of the equation of success. Not the whole equation.

I knew and worked with an autistic kid whose IQ was higher than Albert Einstein's. At age eight he read above college level and did high-end mathematics in his head for fun. I want to share an excerpt of what I received from his mother on a tough day. I think she makes a good point.

> So basically I have a genius who when he gets frustrated bangs his head on the floor or wall, screams uncontrollably, hides under a table to rock, plays with his hands as if they were the coolest toys to exist, memorizes every flipping commercial, flaps his arms when he's either happy or mad and can't talk about his feelings without running and screaming. IQ is not everything. (Autism mother, email excerpt.)

Coexisting Diagnoses

This is the second factor that is completely beyond anyone's control. The autism itself and other issues may be manageable when it comes to life success, but there can be other diagnoses in play that are so severe and debilitating that the person is incapable of living a successful life. The issue is that these other diagnostic factors may not be sufficiently managed. Not the autism.

The list of other diagnoses that could come into play causing someone to have problems with life success is significant. The diagnostic manual is a large book. Any one or combination of other diagnoses could be present that makes a critical difference in life success. Often autism takes the blame for something in a person's life when it is in reality some other diagnosis completely. That does not mean a person cannot still be successful. I have seen coexisting severe diagnoses that, like the autism, have been managed with the right treatments. It is however a factor, and a significant one, in life success.

Embrace the Autism

Some people on the autism spectrum fight or deny the idea of their diagnosis. It is not that they think they are not autistic, but more of an emotional denial. They will claim to be just like everyone else, and that life is fine, even when it clearly isn't. Similarly they will say they don't have any problems, it is everyone else who has the problem.

People like this do not do as well as those who come to terms with what it mean to be autistic, and who like who they are. Those who embrace autism not only understand, but embrace the differences which make them who they are as an autistic individual, and openly share their autism with the world. This also brings them to the point in life where they are eager to learn and do what it takes to live a successful life on the autism spectrum.

To be successful we need to know we are different, and be okay with the idea. We need to know what we are not good at, and what we are very good at. We need to stop trying to be like everyone else. We need to be who we are. Yes, we can do most things others can, but we need to do them differently.

Mentored

Mentoring is a relationship where generally a younger less mature person is guided by an older more mature person in life. A mentor is an advisor, sounding board, accountability partner, teacher, friend, and role model. Having this in the life of someone who is struggling to understand people, emotions, culture, and managing life in a non-autistic world can make a huge difference. A mentor is someone other than the parents who shares and reinforces their same values and priorities. They can sometimes accomplish things purely by not being the parent.

It is easy to view a mentoring relationship as one-way, that it is the mentor who gives to the one being mentored. While the person being mentored does gain a lot (that is the point), it is equally true that the mentor gains a great deal too. Being a mentor is not a job or an obligation. It is a relationship. While the role of a counselor or a therapist may include professional detachment, a mentor is right there by the side of the autistic person, rejoicing and cheering, and occasionally shedding sorrowful tears and experiencing sleepless nights. The mentor is in the trenches with the person they are mentoring.

Many men have consciously decided in today's society that the risks of mentoring kids are too great. They have concluded it just isn't worth it. These men have gotten tired of everyone looking at them suspiciously for spending time with children. There are good mentors out there, but it has gotten harder to find people for this calling.

Ownership of Issues

Those who hold themselves accountable for the decisions they make in life do far better than those who do not. There is a segment of the autism population that thinks the world should conform and completely accommodate them and their issues because they are on the autism spectrum. This is not reality, and these people do not do well in life.

Having autism, I am in a small minority of the population. I do not get to make the rules in life. I need to live in the same world, by the same rules, as everyone else. I can rightly say I made a mistake or had a problem because of autism. That is not making an excuse. However, my thought process cannot stop there. I need to be asking myself why the mistake was made, and what I need to do to avoid making the same mistake in the future. I need to fix what I broke, and work to make sure it doesn't happen again.

Person of Faith

As a conservative Christian I do believe that God can and does intervene in people's lives, but that is not what I am talking about here. For the purposes of our conversation I don't care if it is Christian, Jewish, Buddhist, or something I've never heard of. Also, I am not talking about going through external religious rituals. I am talking about an internalization and deep personal faith, no matter the version of that faith.

One way this helps is a realization that the world is not all about me. There are greater purposes and goals in life beyond myself. Another way this helps the autistic person to be successful is that most, if not all, the major faiths of the world offer direction about how we are to live our lives, including the treatment of others. This is an area that those with autism struggle with, and religious teachings and writings can help guide us in successfully navigating life with others.

Confidence

Those who have confidence in themselves, their abilities, and who they are as a person, do better than those who do not. Confidence is not built by "everyone gets a trophy" or telling them how wonderful they are. In many ways these approaches would be counter-productive because they lack credibility, even in the eyes of a child. Confidence is built through genuine accomplishment of difficult tasks.

The way this can be done is by assessing skills and personality, then encouraging and supporting activities that they have a chance at excelling at, which may even be a special interest. (If it isn't, but they are skilled, it may become one.) So much of the autism world is focused on fixing what is "wrong"; not enough emphasis is placed on helping someone thrive at what they are good at. This competence will typically result in increased life confidence, and a more successful life overall.

Determination

When there are obstacles in our way some people fight through them. Some people outsmart them. Some people turn around and walk away. Those who turn and walk away from obstacles and challenges don't do well in life. Those determined to overcome the obstacles will be successful. Not everyone may have natural skill, but if someone is determined enough amazing things can happen.

I work with someone on the spectrum with extreme dyspraxia. They can't run, have trouble with stairs, need help cutting food, and so on. This person was determined to throw and catch. When I began with them, a special soft easy to catch ball, with a perfect throw from a few feet away, with them sitting, might be caught or trapped around ten percent of the time. A throw from them was uncontrollable. I played a lot of fetch, with me in the role of the dog. Now, several years and hundreds of hours later, this person can throw and catch almost as well as I can. Not an athlete, not even close, but competent. This was the result of absolute determination and refusing to give up.

I have applied this same determination throughout my life. It has not been easy, living in a world not set up for autism. There have been a lot of failures, but every time life has knocked me down, I have gotten back up. It hasn't always been fun, and while I have almost been defeated many times, I have always been determined that I will not give up. The very existence of this book is a testament to sheer determination given my extreme writing difficulties.

In an ideal world there would always be a combination of natural ability and hard work. But reality is often different. If someone is determined to have a successful life, will not be defeated, and is working toward success, regardless of their lack of natural ability, they will likely make it and be successful.

Home Life

In autism parent support groups there seems to be this unwritten rule that by having a kid with a diagnosis everyone automatically becomes the most amazing parent on the planet. While many are excellent parents, many are not. There are good and bad parents of autistic kids just as there are good and bad parents of typical kids. At one end of the scale I have been very impressed by some people's parenting skills, and at the other extreme I have had occasion to call child protective services. I would be lying if I pretended that home life, as a whole, does not matter in how successful someone is in life.

Parents who have their own issues reasonably under control and are well-balanced, thoughtful people provide a much better home environment and bring up more successful kids. Sometimes the best way for us to help our kids is to get the help we need in our own lives as adults.

There have been times when I have had to recommend families split, because it was the least bad option. Sometimes a single parent home is better. But least bad, or better, does not equal good. Kids who grow up in a home with two parents who love each other and love them do better in life than those who do not. It may not be fair, but it is reality.

I do not say these things with the idea that there is any such thing as a perfect parent or home. Once I became a parent I felt like I should have gone back to those families I'd worked with in the previous twenty years and apologize. There were things I couldn't understand until I lived them. The kids I work with, I get to give back at the end of the session. But the teen I took into my home was there all day and all night every day of the week. Rules I swore I would not break were tossed out the window within the first month. I was a single parent, having taken in someone in need and raising them as my own. I learned a lot the hard way.

I get that there is no such thing as perfection. That does not change the fact that some homes are better than others, that home environments can be improved, and those kids from the better homes tend to be more successful in life.

36. PERFECTIONISM

"It's not perfect, but it's better than it was."
- Best friend in college

A lot of parents recognize the perfectionism that they see in their kids on the autism spectrum. While typical people can be perfectionists, many are shocked at how extreme perfectionism can be with autism.

When an autistic child makes a mistake it is not simply erased or crossed out. It is scribbled into oblivion, almost to the point of putting a hole in the paper. It is gone forever. Sometimes the paper is ripped to shreds and stuffed in the garbage, and God help anyone who would go to rescue it. With autism things that are not perfect are destroyed and discarded.

Probably the most damaging impact perfectionism has for someone on the autism spectrum is in the area of self-worth. I am not perfect, and can deal with that in a big picture spiritual way quite well. But when it comes to the details of mistakes I have made and what I should have done differently, I don't deal with it so well anymore.

Regardless of the unconditional love we are surrounded with, an internal battle for self-acceptance is always happening. "I am not perfect. Things that are not perfect are destroyed and discarded. [Autism rule.] Will I be destroyed and discarded because I am not perfect?"

While people on the spectrum are known for being honest, we can try to hide things from those we are close to. I once worked with a mother of an eight-year-old who told me her son had accidentally broken a small lamp and tried to hide the pieces in his room. His mother had the attitude that it was an accident and no big deal. She could not understand his overreaction, absolute denial, and even cowering.

It's because it hit his sense of self-worth. He knew he was not perfect. He intellectually knew that his mother knew he was not perfect. However, here he was faced with giving her evidence that he was not perfect. That was too much. He couldn't bear to have his lack of perfection laid bare in front of someone he depended on. Things that are not perfect are destroyed and discarded. Even though he knew he was loved, and intellectually he knew he will not be destroyed and discarded, at the emotional level he couldn't take the risk.

This is even true for things that are not our fault and totally beyond our control. An autistic child that is being bullied often will not tell anyone. This is not because they are afraid the bully will take revenge. It is because of their damaged self-worth. If they are being bullied it reflects that there is something wrong with them. If there was nothing wrong with them they would not be a target. They cannot risk someone they need in life seeing them as less than perfect. As a result they hide the bullying from those closest to them, so as to not reveal the flaw the bully had identified that made them a target.

My best friend in college had a saying: "It's not perfect, but it's better than it was." I assume that was something he grew up with. Over the years we were there I easily heard him say that a thousand times. There was never any judgment. It was simply: "It's not perfect, but it's better than it was."

After all the times I heard him say that I finally began to be able to internalize it. Unknowingly he helped me to function better. I did not need to be perfect. What I did could be less than perfect. I just needed to make things better than they were. If that was not good enough I could then come back and make them better yet.

I still battle perfectionism, but I can function. The saying "It's not perfect but it is better than it was" is likely one of the most important I have heard in my life.

Showing and talking about unconditional love is critical for those close to a person on the autism spectrum. We need to separate the autistic person's self-worth from their actions. "I love you no matter what you do." "I will always love you even if I don't like some of the things you do." This will not eliminate the self-worth problems entirely, but it can keep them from getting worse.

As part of helping our kids with their self-worth – as it ties in to perfectionism – I encourage parents to be open and honest with their kids about their own successes and failures. No one is perfect. We need to model for the autistic people in our lives what it looks like to be a less than perfect person, yet still a person of value. We share from the past. We share what it felt like, and how we handled it, both the good and the bad. We can share from our present lives too. This doesn't mean dumping our problems on them, but modeling how to fail and still have a successful life in the real, imperfect world. Our kids will learn far more by what they see than by what we tell them.

Even with unconditional love and an understanding that it is impossible to be perfect, perfectionism will always be a battle for those of us on the spectrum. It is who we are.

ABOUT THE AUTHOR

- On the autism spectrum himself providing the perspective of an insider.
- Been working with kids since 1985 as a professional and/or volunteer.
- Founded and has run CNY Autism Consulting since 2011.
- Speaks at universities, schools, and agencies.
- Sits on the NY State Department of Education Advisory Council for Post-Secondary Disability Education.
- Experienced in working with those who have coexisting mental health, developmental, and physical diagnoses.
- Experienced in autism crisis management.
- Works with all ages and levels of functioning.
- Mentors two brothers with autism, in their home, his home, and the community.
- Took in and parented an autistic teen.

Also:

- Repeated third grade in school, and was in a self-contained classroom for fourth and fifth grade.
- Couldn't ride a bike until age eleven.
- While repeatedly failing in high school accused of being: lazy, unprepared, unconcerned, and not working to abilities.
- Failed courses in college, graduating with a 2.2 GPA, and not knowing if there would be a diploma until the day before graduation.
- Was fired from multiple jobs, and almost fired from several more.
- Struggles with handwriting to the degree he has difficulty doing much more than signing his name or making a shopping list.
- Most days has a sink piled with dirty dishes.

47423825R00124

Made in the USA
Middletown, DE
06 June 2019